Edexcel GCSE (9–1)
Combined Science

Homework and skills Foundation

Some of the questions help you to develop different skills, shown by the icons below.

 Maths skills

 Knowledge and understanding of practicals

 Reading and writing skills

 Research skills

Published by Pearson Education Limited, 80 Strand, London, WC2R 0RL.

www.pearsonschoolsandfecolleges.co.uk

Text and illustrations © Pearson Education Limited

Typeset by Phoenix Photosetting, Kent

Cover design by Peter Stratton

The rights of Mark Levesley, Penny Johnson, Sue Kearsey, Iain Brand, Nigel Saunders, Sue Robilliard to be identified as authors of this work have been asserted by them in accordance with the Copyright, Designs and Patents Act 1988.

The Publishers would like to thank the following people for their contribution to the text: John Kavanagh, Carol Tear, John Ling, Mary Jones, James de Winter, James Newell and Miles Hudson.

First published 2018

21 20 19 18

10 9 8 7 6 5 4 3 2 1

ISBN: 978 1 292 24710 6

Cover image: Science Photo Library Ltd: NASA

All other media © Pearson Education

Pearson Education Limited is not responsible for the content of any external internet sites. It is essential for tutors to preview each website before using it in class so as to ensure that the URL is still accurate, relevant and appropriate. We suggest that tutors bookmark useful websites and consider enabling students to access them through the school/college intranet.

Acknowledgement
Page 18 © Public Health Wales, http://www2.nphs.wales.nhs.uk:8080/, Seasonal influenza in Wales 2016/17 Annual Report , P. 12.

A note from the Publishers: Pearson Education Limited: This resource is based on the March 2016 accredited version of the specification. The homework activities in this resource have not been reviewed or endorsed by Edexcel and should not be considered as being published by Edexcel.

Copies of official specifications for all Edexcel qualifications may be found on the website: www.edexcel.com

While the Publishers have made every attempt to ensure that advice on the qualification and its assessment is accurate, the official specification and associated assessment guidance materials are the only authoritative source of information and should always be referred to for definitive guidance. Pearson examiners have not contributed to any sections in this resource relevant to examination papers for which they have responsibility. Examiners will not use this resource as a source of material for any assessment set by Pearson.

The homework activities are not required to achieve this Pearson qualification. It is not the only suitable material available to support the qualification, and any resource lists produced by the awarding body shall include appropriate resources.

1. Label the microscope to show position of the:

a. eyepiece lens

b. objective lens

c. stage

d. slide

e. focusing wheel.

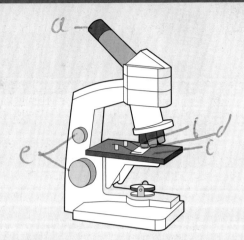

2. The microscope above has an eyepiece lens with a ×5 **magnification**. It has three objective lenses: ×10, ×20 and ×30. When the ×10 objective lens is used, the total magnification is: 5 × 10 = ×50.

a. Calculate the total magnification when the ×20 objective lens is used. Show your working.

5x 20=100

b. Calculate the total magnification when the ×30 objective lens is used. Show your working.

5x 30 = 150

3. Shiv examines some animal hairs using a microscope. Hair X is 20 μm wide and hair Y is 60 μm wide.

a. How many times wider is hair Y compared with hair X? Show your working.

it is 3x wider   20 x3=60

b. Shiv examines hair X using a total magnification of ×150. How wide will the hair appear under the microscope, in micrometres?

3 micrometres

c. Give your answer to part **b** in millimetres. 0.003

d. What total magnification will Shiv need to make hair Y appear 6 mm wide? Show your working.

100x60=6000 = 6mm

4. 1 μm = 1 000 000 pm.

a. What do the unit symbols μm and pm stand for? _____ picometer _____

b. Complete this sentence: 1 μm = 1000 nm and 1 nm = 1 000 pm _____ pm.

5. a. What is an electron microscope? __ it so you can see cells in 3D Not 2D

b. State **two** reasons why an electron microscope can detect more detail inside a cell, compared with a light microscope.

you can see the sell in d 3D perspective

1. a. Label the names of the sub-cellular parts of this cell.

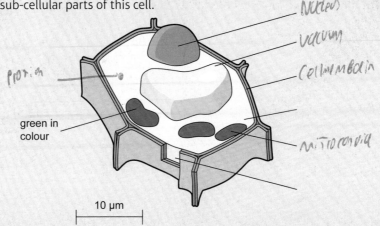

Nucleus
Vacuum
Cell membarin
Mitrocondria
protien
green in colour

10 μm

b. Is this cell from a plant or an animal? Explain your choice. _iT is a plant cell because ɪ has a vacum in The midle_

c. One part can sometimes be seen using a light microscope, but it is not shown here. Draw it on the diagram and label it with its name.

d. What is the function of the part that you have drawn in? _pla iT is protien_

e. What is the function of the largest part inside the cell? _iT controls what Leves The cell and enters_

f. What other parts do both animal and plant cells have that cannot be seen using a light microscope?

g. The function of these parts is to make a certain substance. What substance do they make?

2. A special type of glass slide with a very fine scale is viewed through a microscope. The image below on the left shows what is seen. Human fat cells are then observed using the same magnification, shown below on the right.

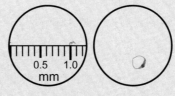

0.5   1.0
mm

a. What is the diameter of the **field of view**? _W 1.3_

b. Estimate the diameter of the fat cell. _0.2_

c. Why is it useful to estimate things in this way, rather than doing careful measurements? _iT might save lots of Time in an exam_

3. Use the **scale bar** on the drawing of the cell at the top of the page to estimate the length of the green sub-cellular structures.

0.5

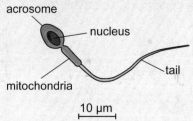

Human sperm cell (magnification × 1000)

1. Human sperm cells are **haploid**. What does this mean?

_____

2. The cells that divide to form **sperm cells** are **diploid**. What must happen during this type of cell division to make **haploid** sperm cells?

_____

3. Sperm cells have several **adaptations** that help them travel through the **oviduct** and fertilise an **egg cell**. Explain how each of these adaptations helps:

a. tail _TO Move ~~FHrough~~ ~~The~~ with easy_____

b. lots of mitochondria _____

c. acrosome _____

_____

_____

4. Measure the length of the sperm in the diagram and then use the magnification to calculate the real length of a sperm. Give your answer in cm, mm and μm.

_____

5. A jelly coat surrounds an egg cell.

a. What is the function of the jelly coat before the egg cell is fertilised?

_____

b. How does the jelly coat change immediately after a sperm cell fuses with the egg cell?

_____

c. What is the function of this change in the jelly coat?

_____

6. The cells lining the oviduct (the tube along which the egg cell moves) have **cilia** in their cell surface membranes. What is the function of the cilia?

_____

Sciences
Homework & skills

CB1e Enzymes and nutrition

1. The diagram shows some large organic (biological) molecules. Add labels to the lines to identify the subunits in each molecule.

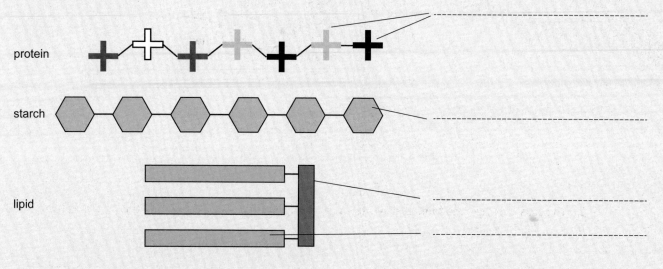

protein

starch

lipid

2. Which kind of large organic molecule are enzymes? _____

3. Enzymes are **biological catalysts**. Explain what this means.

_____

_____

_____

4. Amylase is a digestive enzyme found in humans.

a. In which **two** parts of the human digestive system is amylase found?

_____

b. Which carbohydrate, found in foods such as pasta, is the substrate for amylase?

_____

c. Describe the effect of amylase on this molecule.

_____

_____

5. Some enzymes catalyse reactions in which a molecule is synthesised. Explain what this means.

_____

_____

_____

Sciences **CB1g** Enzyme activity

Homework & skills

1. This graph shows how the rate of reaction of the human amylase enzyme changes with temperature.

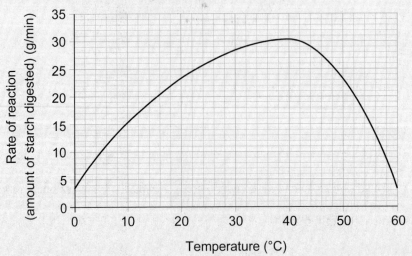

How the rate of starch breakdown using amylase depends on temperature

(Graph: Rate of reaction (amount of starch digested) (g/min) on y-axis from 0 to 35; Temperature (°C) on x-axis from 0 to 60)

a. What is the **optimum temperature** of human amylase? 40

b. Explain what 'optimum temperature' means.

The higest point of the graf

2. This graph shows the effect of substrate concentration on an enzyme-controlled reaction. The dots and shapes show enzyme and substrate molecules. As substrate concentration increases, the number of substrate molecules increases but the number of enzyme molecules stay the same.

Complete the labels to describe why the curve is this shape.

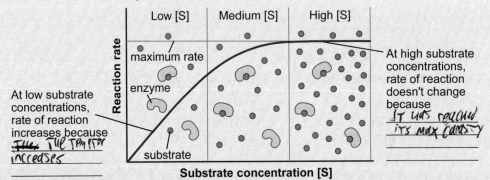

At low substrate concentrations, rate of reaction increases because the the Tempitor incredses

maximum rate
enzyme
substrate

At high substrate concentrations, rate of reaction doesn't change because It was reuched its max cerersty

Substrate concentration [S]

3. Explain why an enzyme-controlled reaction in question **2** stops at very low and very high pHs.

The diagram shows a **partially permeable** membrane separating two glucose solutions.

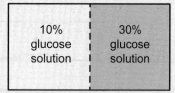

10% glucose solution | 30% glucose solution

1. What is meant by a 'partially permeable membrane'?

_____

_____

2. Glucose molecules are small enough to pass through the partially permeable membrane in the diagram.

a. Circle the transport method by which glucose molecules move through the membrane.

active transport   **diffusion**   **osmosis**

b. In which direction will there be overall movement of glucose molecules in the diagram?

_____

c. Explain your answer to part **b**.

_____

_____

3. In a similar experiment, substance X is used instead of glucose. It is soluble in water but has much larger particles that cannot pass through the partially permeable membrane.

a. Name the process that will occur in this case, in which there is an overall movement of water molecules.

_____

b. In which direction will there be overall movement of water molecules?

_____

c. Explain your answer to part **a**.

_____

_____

4. A piece of potato of initial mass 25 g was placed in water. After 15 minutes its final mass was 50 g. Calculate the percentage gain in mass of the potato.

_____

_____

_____

1. State **two** parts of a cell that make copies of themselves before **mitosis** begins.

_____

2. Look at the diagram below and draw what the cell looks like in the next stage of mitosis.

anaphase   **telophase**

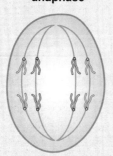

3. Which part of the **cell cycle** is taking place when:

a. the chromosomes line up on the equator of the cell _____

b. the nucleus membrane is breaking down _____

c. DNA and sub-cellular parts are copied _____

d. the cytoplasm of the cell is separated? _____

4. The cells produced from mitosis are genetically identical, **diploid** cells.

a. Describe what 'genetically identical' means.

_____

_____

b. Explain what 'diploid' means and why it is important to the cell. (*Hint:* What would happen to a cell if it was not diploid and went through two rounds of the cell cycle?)

_____

_____

_____

_____

1. Select the statement that best describes how plants grow. Tick **one** box.

   ☐ Cell elongation is followed by cell differentiation then cell division.

   ☐ Cell division is followed by cell elongation and then cell differentiation.

   ☐ Cell division is followed by cell differentiation and then cell elongation.

2. What name is given to the kind of cell division that happens in plant growth?

   _____

   _____

3. Explain why measuring the change in mass of a plant over time can be used to measure the plant's growth.

   _____

   _____

4. The diagram shows a xylem vessel from a plant.

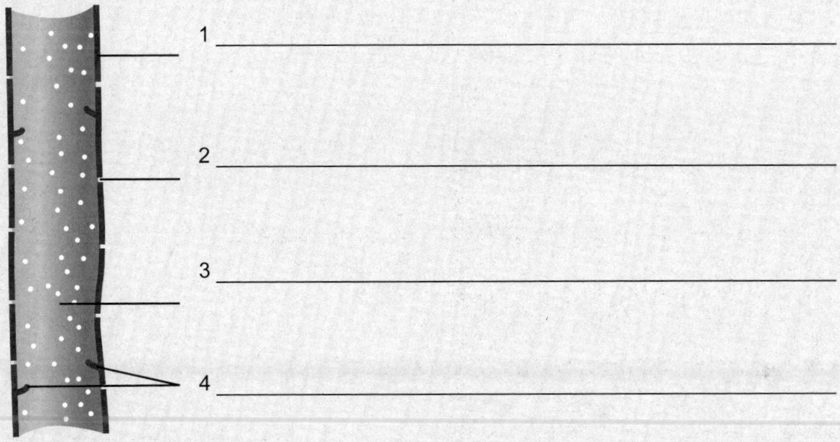

   1 _____

   2 _____

   3 _____

   4 _____

   a. Add labels to the lines to describe the features of a xylem vessel that are not found in other plant cells.

   b. Describe the function of a xylem vessel.

   _____

   _____

   c. Explain how the features of a xylem vessel help it to carry out its function.

   _____

   _____

   _____

   _____

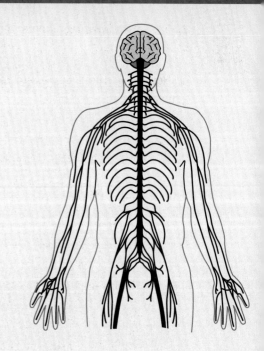

1. On the diagram, label the two parts of the body in the **central nervous system**.

2. Certain cells in your body detect changes in your surroundings (**stimuli**). They send information in electrical signals to the brain. Rearrange the letters on the lines to answer the questions.

a. What cells detect stimuli?

(SCEPTREORCELL) _____

b. What are the electrical signals called?

(SUMSPILE) _____

c. What cells carry these electrical signals?

(ONERUNE) _____

d. What does the brain do with the information that it receives?

(ROSESPECS) _____

3. a. The diagram below shows a sensory neurone. Label the diagram with the following:

axon	axon terminal	dendrite	dendron	receptor cell

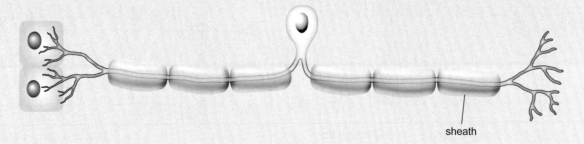

sheath

b. Add arrows below the diagram to show the direction in which electrical signals are transmitted.

c. What substance is the sheath made out of? Tick **one** box.

☐ myelin   ☐ melamine   ☐ mica   ☐ malolactate

d. Describe **two** ways in which the cell is adapted to its function. _____

_____

_____

4. Anthony picks up an ice cube. Explain how Anthony can feel that the ice cube is cold.

_____

_____

_____

_____

1. The table shows the number of chromosomes in the body cells of various animals.

a. How many chromosomes are needed in a pig to contain its entire genome?

_____

Animal	Total number of chromosomes in a normal body cell
fruit fly	4
pig	38
human	46
gypsy moth	62
dog	78

b. Why are the numbers of chromosomes all even numbers?

_____

_____

c. How many chromosomes would you expect to find in each of these cells?

    i   a human body cell _____   **ii**   a dog sperm cell _____

    iii   a gypsy moth egg cell _____   **iv**   a pig zygote _____

2. The drawing below shows a body cell from a fruit fly.

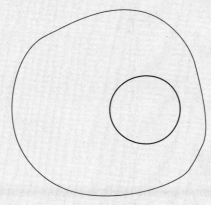

a. Draw in its chromosomes.

b. What long molecule is found inside each chromosome?_____

c. Add labels for: cell membrane, chromosome, cytoplasm, nucleus, position of a gene.

d. What do genes contain the instructions for?_____

e. Unmuddle these letters to give the name of a cell part that joins amino acids together.

BRIEMOOS _____

f. In which part of the cell are these parts found?_____

3. Using **some** of the words from the box, complete the sentences to describe the importance of meiosis.

chromosome	daughter	diploid	eight	father	female	fertilisation	four
haploid	male	meiosis	mitosis	mother	son	two	gametes

A zygote is formed when male and _____ gametes fuse. The zygote divides by _____ to

form an embryo. To make sure the zygote is _____ (2n) the gametes must be _____ (1n).

So, _____ is used to make gametes. This process produces _____ haploid cells.

There are two copies of each _____ in a gamete-making cell. The two copies are slightly different.

The different copies are randomly sorted into the _____ cells and so one gamete-making cell will

produce _____ that contain different mixtures of chromosomes.

1. Rearrange the letters to make the words described in the clues.

   a. Where most DNA is found in a eukaryotic cell. SUNCLUE _____

   b. A structure made of DNA packaged up with proteins. MRSMOOECHO _____

   c. A base found in DNA. STONYICE _____

   d. A molecule made of many similar units joined in a chain. ROPYELM _____

2. Rewrite the following sentences, correcting the mistakes.

   a. A DNA molecule forms a single helix.

   _____

   b. DNA is made of a sugar, a nitrate group and five different sorts of bases.

   _____

   c. A short length of DNA containing instructions for a protein is called a chromosome.

   _____

3. The diagram below shows a single strand of DNA.

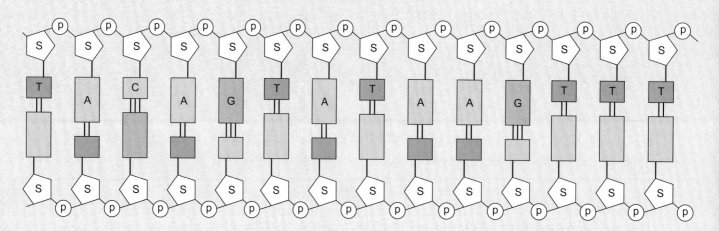

   a. On the diagram, fill in the letters for the complementary base pairs.

   b. How are the bases joined together? _____

 4. a. When scientists extract DNA from cells, they need to add chemical substances that will break down two sets of membranes. Describe where these membranes are found.

   _____

   _____

   _____

   b. To extract pure DNA, scientists add enzymes called proteases. These break down proteins. Explain why this step is needed.

   _____

   _____

   _____

Sciences **CB3c** Alleles
Homework & skills

1. Use words from the right-hand box to complete the labelling on the diagram below. Use each word once.

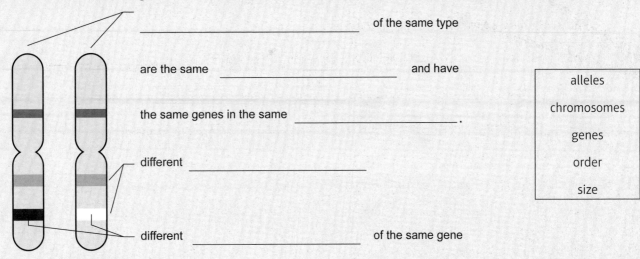

_____ of the same type

are the same _____ and have

the same genes in the same _____ .

different _____

different _____ of the same gene

| alleles |
| chromosomes |
| genes |
| order |
| size |

2. Look at this list of genotypes.

| Mm | MM | mm | PP | Pp | pp | QQ | qq | Qq |

a. Circle the genotypes that are homozygous for the dominant allele.

b. Underline the genotypes that are heterozygous.

3. Circle the wrong word in each sentence and write down the correct word.

a. A genotype is the proteins found in an organism. _____

b. The characteristics of an organism caused by alleles are its genotype. _____

4. a. Complete the genetic diagram for this monohybrid cross between two pea plants. The allele for yellow peas (Y) is dominant. Peas that are homozygous for the recessive allele (y) have green peas.

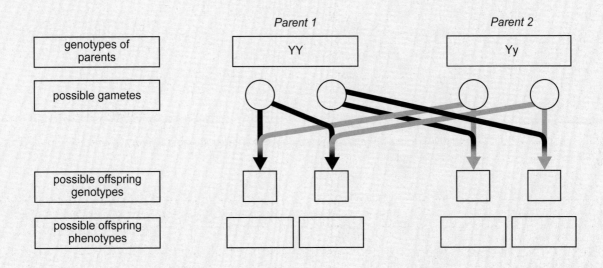

Parent 1   Parent 2

genotypes of parents   YY   Yy

possible gametes

possible offspring genotypes

possible offspring phenotypes

b. Explain why none of the plants will have green peas.

_____

_____

_____

1. Some inherited characteristics are controlled by single genes, others are caused by multiple genes.

a. Circle the characteristic that is controlled by a single gene:

> eye colour   height   cystic fibrosis   skin colour

b. Are most human characteristics controlled by single genes or multiple genes?_____

2. The Human Genome Project was completed in 2003. Circle the letter that shows the main aim of this project:

A. to name all the human genes

B. to map all the human genes that cause disease

C. to map all the base pairs in one human genome

D. to define what is meant by the human genome.

3. Comparing different human genomes shows that there may be differences caused by mistakes made when the DNA is copied during cell division. What is the name for this kind of mistake in DNA?

_____

4. Although there are differences in the DNA between different people, the people may look very similar. Explain why.

_____

5. The table shows some results of a genome test for one person. Clopidogrel, simvastatin and warfarin are medicines that a doctor may give a patient to treat some diseases. Information from a genome test can help the doctor decide how to treat a patient.

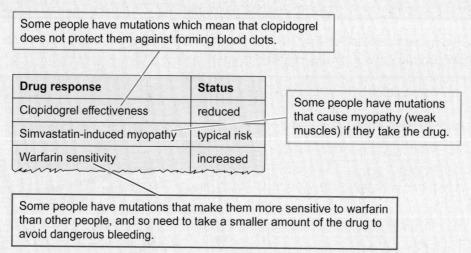

Some people have mutations which mean that clopidogrel does not protect them against forming blood clots.

Drug response	Status
Clopidogrel effectiveness	reduced
Simvastatin-induced myopathy	typical risk
Warfarin sensitivity	increased

Some people have mutations that cause myopathy (weak muscles) if they take the drug.

Some people have mutations that make them more sensitive to warfarin than other people, and so need to take a smaller amount of the drug to avoid dangerous bleeding.

a. Which of these drugs might the doctor decide not to give the patient because it may not work well?

_____

b. Explain your answer to part a.

_____

c. Describe one other way that information from genomes could help in medicine.

_____

1. Use the information in parts **a–c** below to add **binomial** names to the correct places in the diagram.

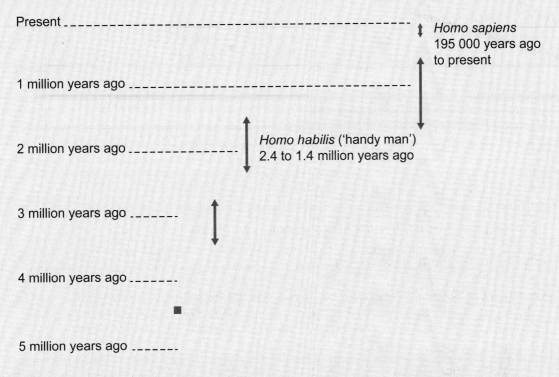

Present

1 million years ago

2 million years ago

3 million years ago

4 million years ago

5 million years ago

Homo sapiens
195 000 years ago
to present

Homo habilis ('handy man')
2.4 to 1.4 million years ago

a. *Australopithecus afarensis* was an ancestor of modern humans that lived 3.9 to 3.0 million years ago.

b. A fossil of *Ardipithecus ramidus* has been dated as 4.4 million years old.

c. Fossils show that *Homo erectus* was found throughout Asia 1.8 to 0.5 million years ago.

2. Which two **species** in the diagram lived at the same time? _____

3. Some of these species have nicknames, such as 'handy man' and '**Lucy**'. Add the nickname 'Lucy' and the nickname for *Ardipithecus ramidus* to the diagram above.

4. What is the binomial name for modern-day humans? _____

5. Name two human-like species discovered by scientists with the surname Leakey.

_____

6. Describe one way human-like species changed over time that we can tell from fossils.

_____

7. Some scientists think that the species in the diagram above evolved into each other. Others disagree. Give one reason why scientists cannot be sure about the exact **evolution** of the species that led to humans.

_____

8. What does the way stone tools used by human-like species changed suggest about human evolution?

_____

_____

1. Add a tick to the column in the table that identifies the correct **kingdom** for each organism.

Organism	animals	plants	fungi	protists	prokaryotes
a. Multicellular organism that lives attached to rotten trees, on which it feeds. Its cells have a nucleus but not chloroplasts.					
b. Its cells have a nucleus but do not have cell walls. The organism has tissues and organs.					
c. Single-celled organism that has a large loop of DNA in its cytoplasm.					
d. Its cells have cell walls made of cellulose and contain a large permanent vacuole.					
e. Its cells have mitochondria but not chloroplasts, nor cell walls.					
f. Unicellular organism that has a nucleus and cytoplasm, but its cell surface membrane is covered by a layer of proteins and not a cell wall.					

2. Some members of the animal kingdom are listed in the box.

blackbird	gorilla	lion	robin	tiger

a. Divide them into two groups. Circle members of one group and draw squares around the other.

b. How have you decided on which group to put each animal in?_____

_____

c. Complete this sentence: The last two groups that organisms are sorted into are called the **genus** and the

_____

d. The binomial name for lions is *Panthera leo*. What genus do lions belong to? _____

3. Look at the two organisms below.

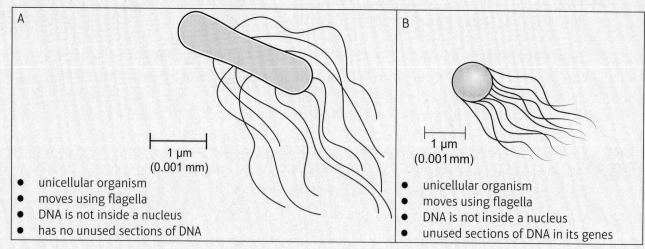

A
- unicellular organism
- moves using flagella
- DNA is not inside a nucleus
- has no unused sections of DNA

1 µm
(0.001 mm)

B
- unicellular organism
- moves using flagella
- DNA is not inside a nucleus
- unused sections of DNA in its genes

1 µm
(0.001 mm)

a. When these two organisms were first discovered they were both classified as prokaryotes. State why.

_____

b. Explain how genetic analysis showed that the organisms are different.

_____

c. They are now separated into two domains: Bacteria and Archaea. State the name of the third **domain**.

_____

1. Draw lines to match the words with their meanings.

genetic engineering	all the DNA in an organism
genome	the amount of useful product that you can get from something
artificial selection	altering the genome of an organism by adding genes from another species
yield	a version of a gene
allele	when people choose organisms with certain characteristics to breed

2. The drawing shows a shire horse. Shire horses were selectively bred to pull heavy carts, ploughs and farm machinery. In the 19th century there were hundreds of thousands of shire horses in the UK. Today there are only about 3500.

a. Suggest what characteristics were selected for to breed shire horses.

_____

_____

_____

b. Suggest why there are fewer shire horses today. _____

_____

c. Shire horses are often kept on rare-breed farms along with other breeds of farm animal that are no longer popular. Give one reason why old breeds are kept.

_____

_____

3. In 2011, pistachio nut farmers in Australia were expecting a good yield from their trees because of excellent weather. Instead, they lost almost half of their crop of pistachios to disease. Suggest what may have happened.

_____

_____

4. In August 2013, some activists in the Philippines destroyed a field of GM Golden Rice plants that were part of a trial. Give one reason why the activists were against the growing of GM crops.

_____

_____

Edexcel GCSE (9-1)
Sciences
Homework & skills

CB5a Health and disease

CB5 Health, Disease and the
Development of Medicines

1. The World Health Organization defines **health** as a state of complete physical, mental and social well-being. Draw lines to link each example to the type of well-being it relates to.

Type of well-being

physical

mental

social

Examples

good self-esteem

having lots of friends

not being ill

not smoking

being comfortable about where you live and work

exercising regularly

2. Cancer and flu are both **diseases** of people.

a. What is meant by the term disease?

_____

_____

b. Many forms of cancer are **non-communicable diseases**. Explain what non-communicable means.

_____

_____

c. The graph shows the proportion of people in Wales who had flu when they saw their doctor, for the years 1987–2011.

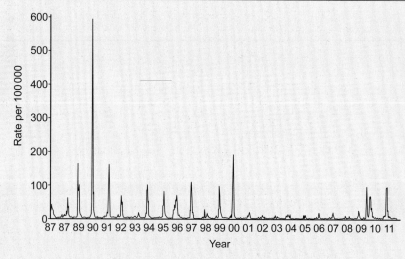

Proportion of people in Wales with flu diagnosed by a doctor.

What evidence in the graph supports the fact that flu is a **communicable disease**?

_____

_____

1. The graph shows the risk of heart failure in women in a study that lasted for about 20 years. The women were measured and grouped into three categories: obese, overweight, normal.

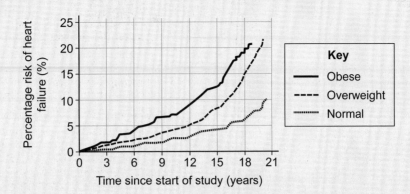

*How risk of heart failure changes over time for women in different **body mass index (BMI)** categories.*

a. Suggest which measurements were taken so that the women could be grouped into the categories.

_____

b. Tick the statements that are conclusions that can be drawn from the graph. (Tick all correct answers.)

☐ A woman who is obese will have heart failure within 18 years of being studied.

☐ Women who are obese have a greater risk of heart failure than women who are normal weight.

☐ The risk of heart failure after 15 years from the start of the study is about twice as large for obese women as for women of normal weight.

☐ The risk of heart failure after 15 years from the start of the study is about three times as large for obese women as for women of normal weight.

2. Describe one treatment that someone with heart failure may be given and explain how this treatment would help them get better.

_____

_____

_____

3. To help prevent heart failure, a doctor might tell obese people to change their diet, increase exercise and stop smoking. Explain why this might help.

Change diet, because _____

_____

Increase exercise, because _____

_____

Stop smoking, because _____

_____

1. Below is a list of diseases.

malaria _____ tuberculosis _____ chalara dieback _____ AIDS _____

a. Write B beside the disease caused by a bacterium.

b. Write F beside the disease caused by a fungus.

c. Write P beside the disease caused by a **protist**.

d. Write V beside the disease caused by a **virus**.

2. The diseases in question **1** are caused by pathogens.

a. What is a pathogen?

_____

b. Explain why these diseases are communicable.

_____

_____

3. Draw lines to link each disease with the signs of that disease.

Name of disease	Symptoms
chalara dieback	damaged blood and liver cells
malaria	**diarrhoea** (watery faeces)
tuberculosis	loss of leaves, lesions in bark
cholera	lung damage, blood in mucus after coughing, weight loss

4. Infection with **HIV** can lead to the onset of **AIDS**, when other pathogens can infect the body. Which effect of HIV infection makes it easier for other pathogens to cause illness?

_____

1. Complete the table to show how the body is protected against infection by pathogens.

Protection	Where found in body	How this protects the body
hydrochloric acid		
mucus		
lysozymes		
cilia		

2. In the left-hand column of the table above, write P if the protection is a **physical barrier**, or C if the protection is a **chemical defence**.

3. Describe how one other physical barrier of the body protects against infection.

_____

_____

4. HIV and *Chlamydia* are two infections of humans that are transmitted in the same way.

a. HIV is a virus. Which type of organism is *Chlamydia*? _____

b. Tick all the boxes below that show someone at risk of being infected with HIV or *Chlamydia*.

☐ a person under 25 who is not sexually active

☐ the developing fetus of a pregnant woman who has the disease

☐ any person who has kissed someone with the disease

☐ any person who has unprotected sex with an infected person

c. Describe, with a reason, one way of preventing the transmission of both pathogens.

_____

_____

5. Smoking damages **ciliated cells** in the tubes of the lungs. Explain why this can lead to lung infections.

_____

_____

The graph below shows how the body responds by producing **antibodies** when it is infected by a pathogen. Use the graph to help you answer questions **2–6**.

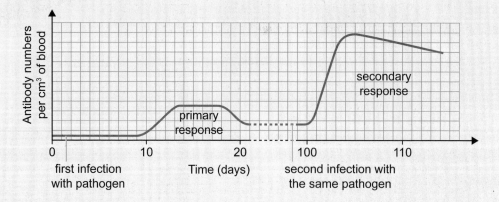

1. Which cells produce antibodies to pathogens? _____

2. Explain why the antibody numbers increase in the primary response.

_____

_____

3. Suggest on which day the first infection by the pathogen was cleared from the body.

_____

_____

4. Why do the antibody numbers remain higher after the first infection than before it?

_____

_____

5. Describe two differences between the responses after the first and second infection by the same pathogen.

Difference 1: _____

Difference 2: _____

6. **a.** If the body were infected by a different pathogen for the first time, would the immune response to that infection look like the primary response or **secondary response** in the graph?

_____

b. Explain your answer to part **a**.

_____

_____

7. Describe how **immunisation** with a **vaccine** helps to make you **immune** to a pathogen.

_____

_____

_____

Edexcel GCSE (9-1)
Sciences **CB6a** Photosynthesis
Homework & skills

**CB6 Plant
Structures and
their Functions**

1. Write down the word equation for **photosynthesis**.

_____ + _____ → _____ + _____

2. The diagram shows the arrangement of different tissue layers in a leaf.

a. Write the letter for the layer that contains the most **chloroplasts**. _____

b. Write the letter for the layer in which most photosynthesis occurs. _____

c. Write the letter for the layer that contains **stomata**. _____

3. a. From which sugar do plants make **starch**? _____

b. Name one other substance made from this material. _____

c. What do plants use starch for? _____

4. What process do plants use to release energy as they need it? _____

5. a. What is **biomass**? Tick the best answer.

☐ the materials in an organism ☐ the waste produced by an organism ☐ another word for energy ☐ the mass of material an organism eats

b. Explain why animals need plant biomass. _____

_____

c. Where does all the energy in a garden **food chain** originally come from? _____

6. Complete the table below to explain how each of the features of a leaf is an adaptation for photosynthesis.

Feature	How this helps photosynthesis
large surface area	
chlorophyll	
stomata	

7. In photosynthesis, the reactants store less energy than the products. What sort of process is this? Tick **one** box.

☐ exothermic ☐ homeothermic ☐ mesothermic ☐ endothermic

1. Complete the sentences, using words from the box, to explain why some factors can alter the **rate** of photosynthesis. Each word can be used once, more than once or not at all.

carbon	energy	enzymes	faster	high
higher	little	low	lower	slower	transfers

a. Factor: light intensity. Photosynthesis needs the _____ transferred by light. The greater the light intensity, the more energy it _____ (and so the _____ the rate of photosynthesis).

b. Factor: carbon dioxide **concentration**. Photosynthesis uses _____ dioxide. If the concentration of carbon dioxide in the air is too _____, it can stop the rate of photosynthesis being as _____ as it could be.

c. Factor: temperature. Photosynthesis uses _____, which work _____ at _____ temperatures (although they stop working if they get too hot).

2. The graph shows how the rate of photosynthesis changes in some pondweed as the light intensity increases.

a. What units are being used for the rate of photosynthesis?

_____

b. What gas would you expect to find in the bubbles?

_____

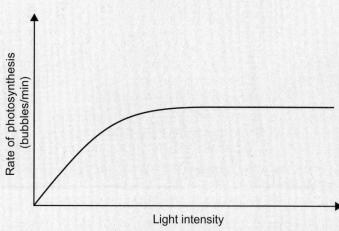

c. The sloping part of the line shows that as light intensity increases, so does the rate of photosynthesis. What is the **limiting factor** in this part of the graph?

_____

d. The horizontal line is caused by carbon dioxide being a limiting factor. Draw another line on the graph to show what happens if the concentration of carbon dioxide is doubled.

3. Bottles of algae in pH indicator solution were placed at different distances from a lamp. The pH in each bottle at the start was 8.4. The pH values after an hour are shown in the table.

Tube	A	B	C	D	E
pH after one hour	8.4	9.1	8.6	8.8	9.0

Suggest which tube was closest to the lamp. Explain your answer. _____

_____

_____

_____

1. Draw lines to match each factor with its effect on the rate of **transpiration** and the explanation of the effect.

Factor	Transpiration rate	Explanation
increasing light intensity	increases	Water vapour outside stomata is reduced, maintaining the concentration gradient.
increasing temperature	decreases	Additional water vapour decreases the concentration gradient.
increasing wind speed	increases	Evaporation and diffusion are faster.
increasing humidity	increases	The stomata open wider.

2. A student uses a **potometer** to measure the volume of water absorbed by a plant shoot in three minutes. She repeats her measurements three times. The volumes are: 12.9 mm^3, 13.4 mm^3 and 13.2 mm^3.

a. Calculate the mean volume of water absorbed per minute.

_____

b. Calculate the mean rate of transpiration in mm^3/min.

_____

c. Give the name of the tubes in a plant that carry water during transpiration. _____

d. As water evaporates from the plant, it pulls more water up through these tubes. Give one reason why the column of water does not break. _____

_____

3. The diagram shows **phloem tissue**. Explain how sucrose is moved in this tissue, by completing the following sentences.

The _____ cells pump sucrose solution into

the _____ cells using _____ transport.

This is why **companion cells** contain many _____. As the

sucrose solution enters, it pushes the contents of the **sieve cells**

either up or down. This process moves sucrose around a plant and

is called _____.

companion cell

sieve cell

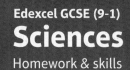

1. Complete the definition below of the term **hormone** using words from the box. You may use each word once, more than once or not at all.

| apocrine | blood | chemical | electrical | endocrine | exocrine | target |

A hormone is a _____ messenger that is released from an _____ gland into

the _____. The hormone travels around the body and when it is detected by a

_____ organ, it changes the way the organ works.

2. Draw lines to link each hormone with where it is produced.

Hormone

| insulin |

| testosterone |

| adrenalin |

| oestrogen |

| thyroxine |

Where hormone is produced

| **thyroid gland** |

| **ovaries** |

| **pancreas** |

| **adrenal glands** |

| **testes** |

3. Growth hormone is produced in the **pituitary gland**.

a. Name **one** tissue or organ that growth hormone affects.

_____

b. Describe how growth hormone affects the body by changing the way that a tissue or an organ works.

_____

_____

4. Give an example of a **sex hormone**.

_____

Edexcel GCSE (9-1)
Sciences
CB7c The menstrual cycle
Homework & skills

**CB7 Animal
Coordination, Control
and Homeostasis**

1. The diagram shows the **menstrual cycle**.

a. Complete the **three** labels by writing what happens during the days indicated.

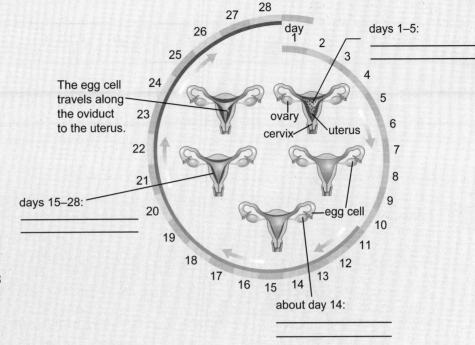

The egg cell travels along the oviduct to the uterus.

days 1–5:
_____
_____

days 15–28:
_____
_____

about day 14:
_____
_____

ovary
cervix
uterus
egg cell

b. Circle the time period in the list below when **fertilisation** is most likely to occur.

days 1–5   days 7–12

days 13–15   days 21–28

2. The graph shows the change in concentration of two hormones during the menstrual cycle.

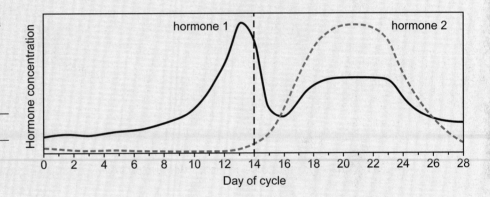

a. Name the hormones.

hormone 1 _____

hormone 2 _____

b. What is triggered by the fall in concentration of hormone 2 towards the end of the cycle?

_____

c. Hormonal **contraception** keeps the concentration of these hormones high. Explain how this reduces the chance of a woman becoming pregnant.

_____

_____

_____

3. a. Explain how **one** named physical barrier method reduces the chance of a woman becoming pregnant.

_____

_____

b. Explain why hormonal contraception methods are usually more effective than barrier methods.

_____

_____

Edexcel GCSE (9-1)

Sciences **CB7f** Type 2 diabetes

Homework & skills

CB7 Animal
Coordination, Control
and Homeostasis

1. Jake has a hip measurement of 102 cm and a waist measurement of 99 cm. Calculate his **waist : hip ratio**.

2. **a.** Jake is 1.82 m tall and has a mass of 87 kg. Calculate his **BMI (body mass index)** using the equation:

b. $BMI = \dfrac{weight\ (kg)}{(height\ (m))^2}$

c. BMI categories are: normal 18.5–24.9, overweight 25.0–29.9, obese ≥30.0. Which category does Jake belong to?

3. The chart shows the relationship between BMI and the relative risk of developing **type 2 diabetes**, compared with people in the lowest category, whose risk is given as 1. A risk of 2 means that the chance of developing type 2 diabetes is twice as great as in the lowest category.

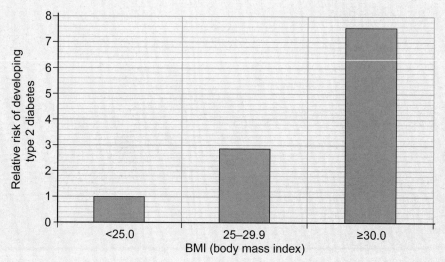

a. State how much greater Jake's risk of developing type 2 diabetes is compared with that of someone with a BMI of 24.0. _____

b. Describe the **correlation** between BMI and risk of type 2 diabetes shown in the chart.

_____

_____

4. **a.** Explain why Jake's doctor has advised him to eat more healthily and to exercise more.

_____

_____

b. Explain how medicine could be used to treat Jake if he developed type 2 diabetes.

_____

_____

5. Explain why Jake should try to reduce his risk of developing type 2 diabetes.

_____

_____

Edexcel GCSE (9-1)

Sciences **CB8a** Efficient transport and exchange

Homework & skills

**CB8 Exchange
and Transport
in Animals**

1. **a.** What gas is needed for **aerobic respiration?**_____

   b. What sugar is needed for aerobic respiration? _____

   c. What waste gas do humans excrete? _____

   d. What waste product is made by breakdown of amino acids? _____

   e. State the reason the body needs to excrete wastes. _____

2. Plants need nitrates to help them make proteins. What are nitrates an example of? _____

3. Lungs have a large **surface area : volume (SA : V) ratio** because they are filled with small pocket-shaped structures (shown in the diagram on the right).

   a. Name this structure.

   _____

   _____

   b. Fill in the missing words in the labels.

   c. Identify gases A and B.

   gas A _____

   gas B _____

Blood enters from the rest of the body with a _____ concentration of carbon dioxide and a _____ concentration of oxygen.

air moves in and out

Blood goes to the rest of the body with a _____ concentration of carbon dioxide and a _____ concentration of oxygen.

net movement of gas A   net movement of gas B

good flow of blood

one-cell thick walls of alveolus and capillary

The alveolus contains a _____ concentration of oxygen and a _____ concentration of carbon dioxide than the blood. Its shape gives it a large surface area.

   d. Underline two phrases that show adaptations that help to increase the rate of **gas exchange**.

   e. For each phrase you have underlined, explain how the adaptation increases the rate of gas exchange.

   _____

   _____

   _____

   _____

4. **a.** Cell S has a volume of 1000 µm³ and its surface area is 600 µm². Calculate its SA : V ratio.

   _____

   b. Cell T is shaped like a cube with sides measuring 20 µm. Calculate its SA : V ratio.

   _____

1. Blood flows from the **vena cava** through the right side of the heart and then through the **pulmonary artery** to the lungs. It then flows back to the heart before being pumped around the body. Number the vessels and heart **chambers** in the order that blood flows through them, starting at the vena cava.

_____ **aorta**   _____ **pulmonary vein**

_____ left **atrium**   _____ right atrium

_____ left **ventricle**   _____ right ventricle

_____ lungs   _____ vena cava

_____ pulmonary artery

pulmonary artery

left ventricle

valve

tendon

2. a. The muscle tissue in the heart does not get tired. Why is this an important adaptation?

_____

_____

_____

_____

b. The muscle tissue needs oxygen. Name one other substance this tissue needs. _____

c. Describe how oxygen is transported from the lungs and heart to a muscle cell. _____

_____

_____

_____

d. Explain why the muscle tissue in the wall of the left ventricle is thicker than in the right ventricle.

_____

_____

_____

3. a. State the function of the **heart valves**. _____

_____

b. Explain why someone might feel short of breath if one of the heart **tendons** breaks. _____

_____

_____

Edexcel GCSE (9-1)
Sciences **CB8d** Cellular respiration
Homework & skills

CB8 Exchange
and Transport
in Animals

1. A respirometer is used to measure the rate of respiration. A simple respirometer is shown below.

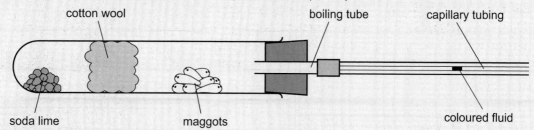

cotton wool   boiling tube   capillary tubing

soda lime   maggots   coloured fluid

In a respirometer, changes in the volume of gases in the boiling tube cause the coloured fluid to move in the capillary tubing. The soda lime absorbs carbon dioxide.

A student sets up the respirometer using 5 g of maggots. After a few minutes, she records the start position of the coloured fluid. The student then measures the position of the coloured fluid five minutes later.

a. Complete the word equation for **aerobic respiration**.

_____ + oxygen → carbon dioxide + _____

b. Why do the maggots need to respire? _____

_____

c. In which parts of maggot cells does aerobic respiration occur? _____

d. Explain the function of the soda lime. _____

_____

e. The coloured fluid moves 30 mm towards the boiling tube during the five minutes.

What change causes this to happen? _____

_____

_____

f. Suggest why it is important that respirometers stay at a constant temperature during repeat experiments.

_____

_____

_____

2. a. Write the word equation for **anaerobic respiration**.

_____

b. Compare the amount of energy released by aerobic and anaerobic respiration.

_____

c. Explain why anaerobic respiration is important for animals. _____

_____

_____

The diagram shows a **food web** for some of the organisms that live in a wood. Wood mice live in small holes in the oak trees and eat acorns (oak seeds), leaves and other foods. Caterpillars eat leaves but often hide under the leaf while they are eating.

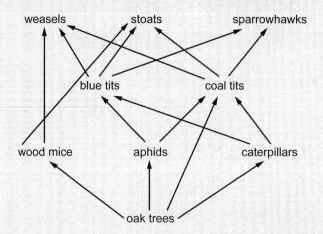

1. a. Organisms depend on each other and the environment for different **resources** to help them stay alive. Which two resources are given in the information above? Tick **two** boxes.

☐ light   ☐ food   ☐ water   ☐ shelter

b. Use the information at the top of the page to link each word with its example.

Term	Example
ecosystem	all the organisms in the wood
population	all the organisms and the environment (e.g. water, light) in the wood
community	all the wood mice in the wood

2. Use the food web above to answer these questions.

a. Name **one** predator of wood mice. _____

b. Name **one** prey of sparrow hawks. _____

c. Give **one** example of a producer in this wood. _____

3. Some students are studying dog violet plants growing below the trees. To estimate the total number of violets in the wood, they take 10 **quadrat samples**. Each quadrat has an area of 1 m². The total area of the wood is 1000 m². Their results are shown in the table. Use the formula below to calculate an estimate for the total population size of violets in the wood.

Quadrat sample	1	2	3	4	5	6	7	8	9	10
Number of violets	0	4	0	0	8	3	0	7	2	6

estimated population size = total number of organisms in samples × $\dfrac{\text{total area of study area}}{\text{total area of quadrats}}$

4. The woodland will be cut down and replaced with houses.

Describe one effect this will have on another species in the food web. Give a reason for your answer.

_____

_____

The table shows the results of a transect survey of low-growing cowslip plants. The transect was placed so that one end was in open meadow and the other inside woodland. The edge of the woodland was about 10 m from the start of the tape.

Use the table to answer the questions.

	Open meadow			Inside woodland		
Distance from tape end (m)	0	4	8	12	16	20
Light intensity (lux)	6430	5673	2554	833	672	587
Soil moisture (%)	28	24	27	31	34	27
Temperature (°C)	14.5	14.0	14.5	13.5	13.0	13.0
Number of cowslip plants (per m²)	15	12	8	2	0	0

1. Describe how you would sample the number of plants at different distances along the transect.

_____

_____

_____

2. Describe the **distribution** of cowslip plants along the transect.

_____

_____

_____

3. The factors measured along the transect are all non-living. What name is given to non-living factors in the environment?

_____

4. Give a reason why each of the measured factors can affect plant growth.

light intensity _____

_____

soil moisture _____

_____

temperature _____

_____

5. **a.** Identify which factor changed most along the transect.

_____

b. Use your answer to part **a** to describe how this factor correlates with cowslip distribution.

_____

_____

_____

1. The food web shows some feeding relationships in an African grassland ecosystem.

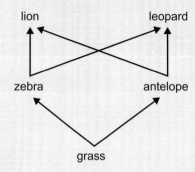

Draw lines to show whether each pair of animals is linked by **competition** or **predation**.

| lion and antelope |

| lion and leopard |

| leopard and zebra |

| competition |

| predation |

2. In one area of an African grassland is a group of five lions and a group of four leopards. A new group of six lions moves into that area of grassland. Predict the effect of the increase in lion population size on the following, giving a reason for your answer.

a. The numbers of zebra and antelope will _____ because

_____

b. The number of leopards will _____ because

_____

3. Competition and predation are **biotic factors** in an ecosystem. What is meant by the term 'biotic factor'?
Tick **one** box.

☐ a factor caused by organisms that affects where organisms live

☐ a factor caused by the environment that affects where organisms live

☐ a factor caused by the environment that harms organisms

☐ a factor caused by plants that affects animals

4. Competition occurs between species when they both need a limited resource. State what is meant by the term 'limited resource'.

_____

5. The following are examples of competition for different resources. Identify the resource that is being **competed** for.

a. Low-growing plants grow more slowly in the shade of taller plants.

_____

b. Conifers have root systems that grow close to the ground surface. In a garden, plants growing next to small conifer bushes often die, even if the bushes do not shade the plants.

_____

_____

Edexcel GCSE (9-1)
Sciences **CB9e** Biodiversity and humans
Homework & skills

**CB9 Ecosystems
and Material
Cycles**

1. a. Draw lines to link each sentence starter with its ending. The four sentences describe how **eutrophication** can cause a decrease in biodiversity.

Eutrophication is …	… food for bacteria, so they grow more rapidly.
Nutrients added to water cause …	… animals cannot get what they need for respiration, and so die.
An increase in dying plants and algae provides …	… the addition of lots of nutrients to an ecosystem such as a river.
Bacteria take lots of oxygen from the water so …	… an increase in the growth of algae and plants in the water.

b. Give one example of a human activity that can cause eutrophication of nearby streams and rivers.

_____

c. Explain why eutrophication can affect biodiversity.

_____

_____

2. Carp is a species of fish that was introduced into the UK in the 14th century.

a. Which scientific term means a species that is introduced to a region? Tick **one** box.

☐ native

☐ non-indigenous

☐ indigenous

☐ competitive

b. Carp were often kept in ponds for **fish farming**. Describe what fish farming means.

_____

_____

c. Carp sometimes escaped from the ponds into nearby streams and rivers. Carp feed on water plants, fish eggs and small water animals. Suggest two reasons why the carp could have caused problems for other fish that lived in the rivers.

Reason 1: _____

_____

Reason 2: _____

_____

d. Salmon is a species of fish that may be caught in the wild or grown in fish farms. Explain how eating farmed salmon can help protect biodiversity in the wild.

_____

_____

1. Select the correct words from the box to complete the following sentences about the **water cycle**.

condensation	transpiration	translocation	evaporation	precipitation

a. Sea water is converted to water vapour in the air by the process of _____.

b. Clouds are droplets of water produced in the air by the process of _____.

c. Soil water is taken into plants and released into the air by the process of _____.

2. The process that converts sea water into water vapour in the air requires a transfer of energy.

Name the main source of that energy. Tick **one** box.

☐ Bunsen burner

☐ Sun

☐ warm soil

☐ living organisms

3. Explain why water droplets in clouds form from water vapour.

_____

_____

_____

4. Most drinking water in the UK comes from rivers, lakes and reservoirs. Over half of the drinking water in Saudi Arabia is produced by **desalination**.

a. State the meaning of desalination.

_____

b. Explain the difference in the sources of drinking water between the UK and Saudi Arabia.

_____

_____

_____

_____

c. Suggest where desalination plants are placed in Saudi Arabia, giving a reason for your answer.

_____

_____

_____

_____

1. Draw lines to link each process to its role in the **carbon cycle**.

photosynthesis	releases carbon dioxide into the air from complex carbon compounds in **fossil fuels**
respiration	transfers complex carbon compounds from one organism to another in **biomass**
combustion	takes carbon dioxide from the air to build carbon compounds in plants and algae
feeding	releases carbon dioxide into the air from complex carbon compounds in living organisms

2. Explain why fossil fuels contain large amounts of carbon compounds.

_____

_____

_____

3. a. Name **two** groups of microorganisms that are **decomposers**.

_____

b. Describe the role of decomposers in ecosystems.

_____

_____

_____

4. Students place some fresh peas in a plastic bag and some sterilised peas in another plastic bag. They measure the temperature of the peas and the carbon dioxide concentration in both bags. They then place the bags inside separate insulated boxes. Two hours later they repeat the measurements. The table shows their results.

	Fresh peas		Sterilised peas	
	Temperature (°C)	Carbon dioxide concentration (ppm)	Temperature (°C)	Carbon dioxide concentration (ppm)
at start	19	400	19	400
2 hours later	24	800	19	400

a. Describe the differences in results for the fresh peas and the sterilised peas.

_____

b. Explain the differences in results.

_____

_____

c. Explain why the bags were placed in insulated boxes during the experiment.

_____

_____

_____

Sciences CC1a States of matter
Homework & skills

1. Name the **state of matter** in which the **particles**:

a. are close together and randomly arranged

_____

b. are regularly arranged

_____

c. have no **attractive forces** between them.

_____

2. Describe what happens to the arrangement and movement of particles when a substance boils.

_____

_____

3. Explain why changes of state are **physical changes**.

_____

4. The diagram shows the cooling curve for substance X.

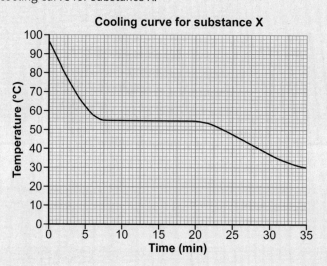

Add the labels **a**, **b**, **c** or **d** to the graph to show:

a. where the substance is freezing

b. the **melting point** of the substance

c. where the substance is in the liquid state and cooling down

d. where the mean energy of the particles is highest.

5. Butane is a fuel. Its melting point is −140 °C and its **boiling point** is −1 °C.

Predict the state of butane at −150 °C and at 25 °C. _____

_____

6. Bromine is in its liquid state at 25 °C. Explain what this tells you about its melting point and boiling point.

_____

_____

1. Circle the **two mixtures** in this list. Explain your choices.

| air | orange juice | silver | sodium chloride | water |

_____

_____

2. Describe the key characteristics of a mixture. Use the key words and phrases given in the box.

| melting temperature   substances   composition |
| range   physical process   separated |

_____

_____

_____

_____

3. Complete the paragraph below using all the words in the box in your answer.

| physical   range   composition   temperature |

Pure substances have a fixed _____. This means that their _____ properties do

not change across the material. This means that melting occurs at a sharp, single _____.

In mixtures, melting occurs over a _____ of temperatures.

4. Look at this graph.

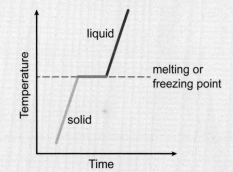

a. Is this a heating curve for a pure substance or a mixture?

_____

b. Explain what the shape of the graph tells you.

_____

_____

_____

_____

Edexcel GCSE (9-1)

Sciences   **CC2b** Filtration and crystallisation

Homework & skills

CC2 Methods of
Separating and
Purifying Substances

1. Match each word to the correct definition.

solute	material remaining in the filter after mixture has passed through it
solution	solution passing through a filter
insoluble	formed when a substance has dissolved in a liquid
residue	substance that has dissolved in a liquid to make a solution
filtrate	describes a substance that cannot be dissolved in a certain liquid
solvent	the liquid in which a solute dissolves to make a solution

2. The list below shows the steps for separating a mixture of sand and salt. Number the steps to show the correct order starting with 1.

crystallisation [   ]   crushing [   ]   dissolving [   ]   heating [   ]   filtration [   ]

3. Put ticks in the correct boxes to show whether each type of mixture can be separated by filtration and/or by crystallisation.

Method of separation	Filtration	Crystallisation
a. Large particle, insoluble solids from a liquid		
b. Soluble salts from a solution		
c. Insoluble impurities from a salt solution		

4. Draw and label a diagram to show how you would set up equipment to filter and crystallise a mixture of salt, sand and water to get samples of salt and sand.

5. List **two hazards** for filtration and crystallisation. For each hazard, state how the risk can be reduced.

Hazard:	Ways of reducing the risk:

The method below can be used to extract perfumed oils from plant material. It is called *steam* distillation. Read the method and then answer the questions. (Do not carry out the practical yourself.)

Apparatus
- a large saucepan with a lid (it is best if there is a handle in the middle of the lid)
- a small, flat-bottomed ceramic dish
- a small cup
- some ice for cooling
- plant material with a perfume (e.g. rose petals or the outer skin of an orange)

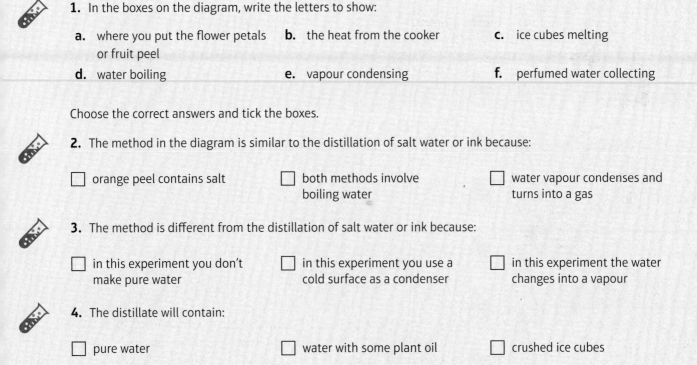

Method

A. Put the dish upside down in the centre of the pan as shown in the diagram.

B. Put the cup on top of the dish – this will be used to collect the perfumed liquid.

C. Fill the pan to about a quarter full with water. Make sure the cup is above the level of the water.

D. Cut the flower petals, or fruit rind, into strips and put them in the water.

E. Put the lid on the pan upside down – the handle on the lid should be above the cup.

F. Bring the water to the boil. When the water starts to boil, fill the lid of the pot with crushed ice.

G. Let the liquid simmer on a medium heat.

H. Collect the distillate from the cup at regular intervals by using a syringe or by swapping the cups over.

Questions

1. In the boxes on the diagram, write the letters to show:

   a. where you put the flower petals or fruit peel   **b.** the heat from the cooker   **c.** ice cubes melting

   d. water boiling   **e.** vapour condensing   **f.** perfumed water collecting

Choose the correct answers and tick the boxes.

2. The method in the diagram is similar to the distillation of salt water or ink because:

   ☐ orange peel contains salt   ☐ both methods involve boiling water   ☐ water vapour condenses and turns into a gas

3. The method is different from the distillation of salt water or ink because:

   ☐ in this experiment you don't make pure water   ☐ in this experiment you use a cold surface as a condenser   ☐ in this experiment the water changes into a vapour

4. The distillate will contain:

   ☐ pure water   ☐ water with some plant oil   ☐ crushed ice cubes

5. **a.** State **one** hazard in this experiment.

   _____

   b. Describe how someone doing this experiment could reduce the risk of harm from this hazard.

   _____

   _____

1. Atomic structure is a good example of a theory that has changed over the last 200 years. Our current model includes **subatomic particles**.

Circle the statements in the box that describe any of Dalton's original ideas about **atoms** that have been changed.

Atoms of **elements** are identical.	Atoms contain charged particles.
Most of an atom is empty space.	Atoms are indestructible.

2. The table has eight statements about atoms. Four of them are true but the others are false. Put a tick in the correct box for each statement. The first one has been done for you.

		True	False
a.	The **nucleus** of an atom contains chromosomes.	☐	☑
b.	All atoms contain **protons**.	☐	☐
c.	Atoms are big enough to see.	☐	☐
d.	**Electrons** are arranged in shells around the nucleus.	☐	☐
e.	Electrons have a larger mass than protons or neutrons.	☐	☐
f.	Electrons have a **relative charge** of +1 and a **relative mass** that is usually ignored (it is 'negligible').	☐	☐
g.	**Neutrons** are electrically neutral.	☐	☐
h.	**Protons** have a relative charge of +1 and a relative mass of 1.	☐	☐

3. Look at each of the false statements in question **2**. For each one, write a correct version of the statement. For example, the statement 'The nucleus of an atom contains chromosomes.' is false. A possible correct statement is shown below.

Correct statement: **a.** The nucleus of an atom contains protons and neutrons.

Correct statement: _____

_____

Correct statement: _____

_____

Correct statement: _____

_____

1. Name the subatomic particle(s) that:

a. have no charge _____

b. have very little mass _____

c. make up most of the mass of an atom. _____

2. Use the diagram of the atom shown here to answer the following questions.

a. Name parts **A** and **B** in the diagram.

A _____

B _____

b. Which particles are found in part **A?**

_____

3. Complete the table below by inserting the missing **atomic numbers** and **mass numbers**.

Element	Number of ...			Atomic number (Z)	Mass number (A)
	protons	neutrons	electrons		
nickel	28	30	28		
oxygen	8	10	8		
osmium	76	114	76		
tin	50	68	50		
boron	5	6	5		
mercury	80	121	80		

4. A particular iron atom can be described as $^{56}_{26}$Fe. Work out its numbers of:

a. protons _____

b. neutrons _____

c. electrons. _____

Sciences   CC4a Elements and the periodic table
Homework & skills

1. Each element is represented by its own chemical symbol. The noble gases (helium, neon, argon, krypton, xenon) had not been discovered when Mendeleev produced his tables in 1869 and 1871.

a. Write down the chemical symbols for these elements. (Refer to the periodic table on page 112 if you need to.)

_____

b. What do these chemical symbols have in common?

_____

c. Radon, Rn, is another noble gas. It was discovered after the discovery of radium, a radioactive metal. Suggest why the chemical symbol for radon does not fit the pattern described in part **b**.

_____

2. Dmitri Mendeleev produced a **periodic table** in 1871. Part of this table is shown below.

Li 7	Be 9.4	B 11	C 12	N 14	O 16	F 19
Na 23	Mg 24	Al 27.3	Si 28	P 31	S 32	Cl 35.5
K 39	Ca 40	Eb? 44	Ti 48	V 51	Cr 52	Mn 55

a. What do the numbers shown here represent?

_____

b. What do the elements in each column have in common?

_____

c. Mendeleev predicted the existence of an element between calcium, Ca, and titanium, Ti. He called this undiscovered element eka-boron, Eb. Suggest why he predicted a number of 44 for this element.

_____

3. Mendeleev predicted the existence of eka-silicon, which he thought should fit between silicon and tin.

Element	Density of element (g/cm³)	Density of its chloride (g/cm³)	Boiling point of its chloride (°C)
silicon	2.3	1.48	58
eka-silicon (**prediction**)			
tin	7.4	2.22	114

a. For each of the three properties in the table above, calculate the mean of the values for silicon and tin.

Write your answers in the table as predictions for eka-silicon.

b. The table below shows some properties of germanium, discovered in 1886 by Clemens Winkler.

Element	Density of element (g/cm³)	Density of its chloride (g/cm³)	Boiling point of its chloride (°C)
germanium	5.3	1.88	86

Germanium was Mendeleev's predicted eka-silicon. Why did its discovery support Mendeleev's ideas?

_____

Edexcel GCSE (9-1)

Sciences
Homework & skills

CC4c Electronic configurations
and the periodic table

CC4 The Periodic Table

Use this short-form periodic table to help you answer the questions. It shows symbols and atomic numbers.

group numbers

		1	2	3	4	5	6	7	0
1		H 1							He 2
2		Li 3	Be 4	B 5	C 6	N 7	O 8	F 9	Ne 10
3		Na 11	Mg 12	Al 13	Si 14	P 15	S 16	Cl 17	Ar 18
4		K 19	Ca 20						

period numbers

1. State what is meant by the term '**electronic configuration**'.

_____

2. Write the electronic configurations for the following elements:

a. helium   _____

b. carbon   _____

c. oxygen   _____

d. chlorine   _____

e. calcium.   _____

sulfur

3. In the box on the right, draw the electronic configuration for sulfur.

4. The table below shows the electronic configurations for three different elements.

Element	lithium	sodium	potassium
Electronic configuration	2.1	2.8.1	2.8.8.1

In terms of their electronic configurations, explain which group these elements belong to.

_____

_____

5. The table below shows the electronic configurations for four different elements.

Element	lithium	beryllium	nitrogen	neon
Electronic configuration	2.1	2.2	2.5	2.8

In terms of their electronic configurations, explain which period these elements belong to.

_____

_____

Sciences   CC5a Ionic bonds

Homework & skills

1. Complete this sentence about **ions**.

Ions are atoms that have become _____ as they have _____ or gained electrons.

2. If an atom gains an electron, what is the charge on the ion? _____

3. **Cations** are positively charged ions. What are negative ions called? _____

4. Complete the table below. Some boxes have been completed for you.

	Group 1	Group 2	Group 6	Group 7
Example atom			S	
Ion charge	1+	2+	2–	
Example ion	Li⁺	Mg²⁺		F⁻

5. Sodium reacts with chlorine to form sodium chloride. This contains sodium ions, Na⁺, and chloride ions, Cl⁻.

a. Complete the following sentence by crossing out the incorrect words in the brackets.

During the formation of sodium chloride, electrons are transferred from [sodium/chlorine] atoms to [sodium/chlorine] atoms.

b. Explain why the sodium ions and chloride ions are attracted to each other.

6. Complete the diagrams below to show a magnesium atom and an oxygen atom forming a magnesium ion and an oxide ion.

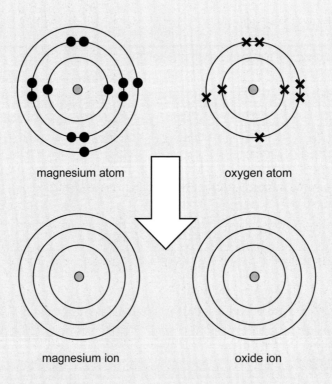

magnesium atom   oxygen atom

magnesium ion   oxide ion

Symbols of some ions:	Na^+ K^+ Mg^{2+} Ca^{2+} Cl^- Br^- I^- O^{2-}

1. Use the symbols of the ions given above to work out the formula of:

a. sodium iodide _____   **c.** magnesium oxide _____

b. potassium oxide _____   **d.** calcium bromide_____

2. The ions in an ionic compound are arranged in a lattice. On the diagram below, add + signs and – signs to show the arrangement of positively charged ions and negatively charged ions in a lattice.

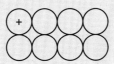

3. Complete the sentences below using words from the box.

atoms   attraction   high   ions   large   low   molecules   repulsion   small   strong   weak

Ionic compounds have _____ melting points. There are _____ electrostatic forces of _____

between the _____ so a _____ amount of energy is needed to separate them.

4. The circuit on the right can be used to see if an **aqueous solution** of a substance conducts an electric current.

Add the missing labels to complete the diagram.

5. Which of these is true for all ionic compounds? Circle the correct answer.

Ionic compounds do not conduct electricity when solid, because:

A. electrons can flow through the gaps in the lattice

B. they contain a metal, and metals conduct electricity

C. the atoms cannot move

D. the ions cannot move.

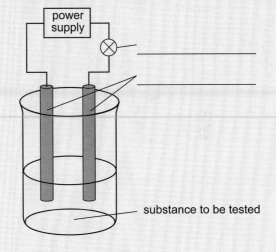

substance to be tested

6. Explain why ionic compounds conduct electricity when they are dissolved in water.

_____

7. The melting point of potassium chloride is 770 °C and that of calcium oxide is 2614 °C.

Suggest a reason why the melting point of calcium oxide is much higher than that of potassium chloride. (*Hint:* look at the symbols for the ions in the box at the top of the page.)

_____

_____

_____

1. Complete the following sentences about bonding and **molecules**.

Substances that are **molecular** are made up of g _____ of atoms held together by

forces called c _____ bonds. These bonds are formed when the atoms

s _____ pairs of electrons, to get a c _____ **outer electron shell** like a

n _____ gas.

The bonded atoms are held together by attractions between their p _____ nuclei and

their n _____ electrons.

2. Some of the elements and compounds listed below contain molecules and some do not. Identify the molecular substances by <u>underlining</u> the *elements* that exist as molecules and by circling the compounds that exist as molecules.

sodium chloride	carbon dioxide gas	copper metal	oxygen gas
magnesium oxide	iron metal	hydrogen gas	water
chlorine gas	nitrogen hydride	nickel fluoride	aluminium metal

3. Complete the **dot and cross diagrams** and the missing part of the compound name in the drawings below.

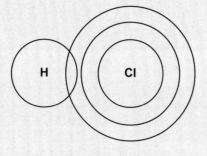

hydrogen chloride

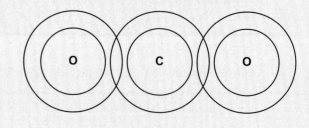

carbon _____

Sciences **CC7a** Molecular compounds
Homework & skills

Use the data from this table to answer Questions **1–3**.

Material	Melting point (°C)	Conductor of electricity	Covalent bonding	Long chains
A	1534	Yes	No	No
B	−56	No	Yes	No
C	113	No	Yes	Yes
D	0	No	Yes	No

1. Use the information in the table to predict which materials (A–D) are:

a. simple molecules _____

b. polymers _____

c. neither simple molecules nor polymers. _____

2. Materials B, C and D do not conduct electricity well. Using information from the table, explain how this might support the idea that these materials contain **covalent bonds**.

_____
_____
_____
_____
_____
_____
_____
_____

3. Materials B and D have low boiling points and low melting points. Use your knowledge of the forces between molecules to explain why this might be the case.

_____
_____
_____
_____
_____

4. Read the paragraph below and underline the correct words in the brackets.

Polymers are **(long/short)** molecular chains made from **(small/big)** molecules called monomers joined together by **(special/chemical)** bonds. Monomers and their polymers have **(the same/different)** melting and boiling points but they are both **(poor/good)** conductors of electricity.

1. Complete the sentences below using words from the box. Each word may be used once, more than once or not at all.

brittle	dull	good	high	low	**malleable**	poor	shiny

a. Most **metals** have a _____ melting point.

b. Metals are _____ when polished and they are _____ conductors of electricity.

c. Solid **non-metals** are _____ when they are hit with a hammer.

d. Non-metals are _____ conductors of electricity.

2. a. The diagram below shows the particles in a metal. Label the particles.

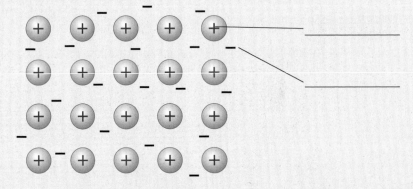

_____

_____

b. Describe how the particles are arranged in a metal.

_____

_____

_____

3. For each of these sentences, state whether it is true or false. If the sentence is false, write the correct sentence on the line below it.

a. All metal atoms need to lose one electron to get a full outer shell. _____

_____

b. The electrons in metals can move around in between the ions. _____

_____

c. A metal contains a layer of negative ions in a sea of electrons. _____

_____

_____

4. Explain, in terms of structure and bonding, why metals are malleable. _____

_____

_____

5. Explain, in terms of structure and bonding, why metals conduct electricity. _____

_____

_____

Sciences **CC7d** Bonding models
Homework & skills

1. Complete the diagrams below showing different models of the bonding and structure of lithium fluoride.

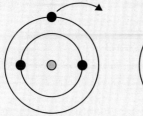
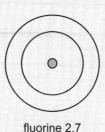
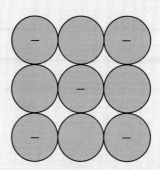

lithium 2.1   fluorine 2.7

a.   b.

2. Complete the descriptions of the structure and bonding of the following substances.

Substance	Melting point (°C)	Boiling point (°C)	Conductor of electricity when:			Type of structure and bonding (covalent, simple molecular; covalent, giant molecular; ionic; or metallic)
			solid	liquid	in solution	
A	1083	2567	yes	yes	insoluble	
B	−107	13	no	no	no	
C	2300	4000	no	no	insoluble	
D	605	1350	no	yes	yes	
E	6	80	no	no	insoluble	

3. Complete the following sentences.

a. Simple molecular substances have low melting points because _____

_____

b. Ionic substances conduct electricity when molten or dissolved in water because _____

_____

4. Complete the missing words in the sentences below, which describe some strengths and weaknesses of the structure and bonding models shown at the top of the page.

a. D_____ and cross diagrams are useful as they show what happens to the e _____ when a

is formed. However, these diagrams do not show the s _____ of the structure
formed by the atoms when they bond.

b. An ionic lattice diagram shows how the oppositely charged i _____ are packed together to form

the l _____ . However, it does not show how the b _____ are formed.

1. Tick (✔) the box to indicate if the following statements are true or false.

	True	False

a. Solutions that contain excess H^+ ions are **acidic**.

b. A solution with a pH of 8 is more **alkaline** than a solution with a pH of 9.

c. The higher the pH, the more acidic the solution.

d. A solution that contains the same concentration of H^+ and OH^- ions is **neutral**.

e. If universal indicator turns orange an alkali is present.

2. Complete the following definitions.

An acid solution has a pH below _____ and contains excess _____ ions.

An alkaline solution has a pH above _____ and contains excess _____ ions.

A neutral solution has a pH of _____ and contains the same _____ of

hydrogen ions and _____ ions.

3. Describe the hazard associated with each of the following symbols.

a.

_____

_____

b.

_____

_____

c.

_____

_____

d.

_____

_____

4. a. Circle the names in the boxes that contain alkalis.

i sour milk, pH 6	ii ice water, pH 7	iii cold tea, pH 6	iv bath salts, pH 8
v fruit juice, pH 5	vi plant food, pH 9	vii ethanol, pH 7	viii drain cleaner, pH 12

b. Which of the above solutions are neither acidic nor alkaline? _____

1. Complete the following neutralisation equations:

   a. zinc oxide + sulfuric acid → _____ _____ + _____

   b. _____ + hydrochloric acid → magnesium chloride + water

   c. H_2SO_4 + NiO → _____ + _____

2. Draw lines to link each of the following statements with the correct terms:

Ion that is removed during neutralisation.	base
Substance that reacts with acids.	acid
Clear liquid formed when a base reacts with an acid.	salt
Ionic compound formed during neutralisation.	neutralisation
Solution that has a pH of less than 7.	hydrogen ion
Happens when a metal oxide is added to an acid.	water

3. The salt copper sulfate can be prepared by reacting an excess of a solid insoluble base with a warm acid solution.

   a. Suggest names for the acid and the base that could be used to make copper sulfate.

   Acid: _____   Base: _____

   b. Suggest a reason why warm acid is used in the reaction.

   _____

   c. Why does the base need to be insoluble?

   _____

   d. Why is an excess of the base used?

   _____

4. During the preparation of copper sulfate, filtration has to be carried out.

   a. Label the diagram opposite to identify the apparatus used.

   b. Name the substance that will be dissolved in the solution in the beaker.

   _____

1. Acid–alkali neutralisation can be modelled using this equation: $H^+(aq) + OH^-(aq) \rightarrow H_2O(l)$

a. Name the ions shown in this equation.

H⁺ ions_____   OH⁻ ions   _____

b. State which reactant, acid or alkali, each ion comes from.

H⁺ ions _____   OH⁻ ions   _____

c. Explain the meaning of the symbols (aq) and (l).

_____

_____

2. Titration must be used to prepare soluble salts from an acid and an alkali. One example of this involves the reaction of dilute sulfuric acid with sodium hydroxide solution.

a. Name the salt formed in this reaction.

_____

b. Describe one reason why titration must be used to prepare this salt using these two substances.

_____

c. Write a word equation for the reaction.

_____

_____

3. A student does a titration using these steps. He:
- adds 25.0 cm³ of dilute sodium hydroxide solution to a conical flask
- adds a few drops of phenolphthalein indicator to the flask
- adds dilute hydrochloric acid until the contents of the flask just changes colour.

a. Name the apparatus he should use to measure the dilute sodium hydroxide solution.

_____

b. Name the apparatus he should use to add the dilute hydrochloric acid to the flask.

_____

c. Describe the colour change he sees at the end-point of the titration.

_____

d. Name a suitable indicator that the student could use instead of phenolphthalein.

_____

The student makes sodium chloride solution using the volumes of acid and alkali he finds by titration. He then heats this solution in an evaporating basin to remove some of the water.

e. Describe what the student should do to obtain dry crystals of sodium chloride.

_____

_____

Sciences
CC8g Solubility

Homework & skills

The box below shows the solubilities of some substances in water. Use this to help you answer the questions.

- All common sodium, potassium and ammonium salts are soluble.
- All nitrates are soluble.
- Most chlorides are soluble except those of silver and lead.
- Most sulfates are soluble except those of lead, barium and calcium.
- Most carbonates and hydroxides are insoluble except those of sodium, potassium and ammonium.

1. In the table below, put a tick in the correct box to show whether the compound is soluble or insoluble.

Compound	Soluble	Insoluble
magnesium chloride		
lead sulfate		
silver chloride		
ammonium carbonate		

2. When barium chloride solution is mixed with sodium sulfate solution, a white precipitate forms.

a. Explain what is meant by a precipitate.

_____

b. Write the word equation for this reaction.

_____

c. Give the name of the precipitate formed in this reaction.

_____

3. Magnesium sulfate solution, $MgSO_4$, reacts with sodium carbonate solution, Na_2CO_3, to form a precipitate.

The word equation is:

magnesium sulfate + sodium carbonate → magnesium carbonate + sodium sulfate

Explain which of the products will form as a precipitate.

_____

_____

4. Describe how to prepare a pure, dry sample of zinc hydroxide from zinc nitrate solution and sodium hydroxide solution.

_____

_____

_____

_____

_____

_____

Element	H	Li	C	N	O	Na	Mg	S	Cl	K	Ca	I
Relative atomic mass (A_r)	1	7	12	14	16	23	24	32	35.5	39	40	127

1. Calculate the **relative formula mass** of each of the following compounds.

a. potassium iodide, KI _____ M_r = _____

b. sodium sulfate, Na_2SO_4 _____ M_r = _____

c. calcium hydroxide, $Ca(OH)_2$ _____ M_r = _____

2. Write the **empirical formula** of each of the following substances.

a. N_2H_4 _____

b. C_6H_{14} _____

c. C_9H_{20} _____

3. Calculate the empirical formula of each of the following substances with the following compositions.

a. 3.60 g of magnesium and 10.65 g of chlorine

_____

_____

_____

_____

b. 9.1 g of lithium and 10.4 g of oxygen

_____

_____

_____

4. State the difference between an empirical formula and a **molecular formula**.

_____

_____

_____

5. Work out the molecular formula of each of the following substances.

a. octane, with empirical formula C_4H_9 and M_r = 114

_____

_____

b. butanoic acid, with empirical formula C_2H_4O and M_r = 88

_____

_____

6. Describe an experiment that will enable you to determine the empirical formula of magnesium oxide. Include the measurements you need to take.

_____

_____

_____

_____

Edexcel GCSE (9-1)

Sciences
CC9b Conservation of mass

Homework & skills

CC9 Calculations
Involving
Masses

Element	H	C	O	Na	Cl	Ca	Zn
Relative atomic mass, A_r	1	12	16	23	35.5	40	65

1. Calculate the mass of oxygen that combines with 20.4 g of magnesium to form 34.0 g of magnesium oxide.

$$2Mg + O_2 \rightarrow 2MgO$$

2. Calculate the minimum mass of sodium hydroxide, NaOH, that is needed to neutralise a **solution** containing 7.3 g of hydrochloric acid, HCl.

$$NaOH + HCl \rightarrow NaCl + H_2O$$

3. Calculate the maximum mass of calcium oxide, CaO, that could be made from 75 tonnes of calcium carbonate, $CaCO_3$.

$$CaCO_3 \rightarrow CaO + CO_2$$

4. 97.5 g of zinc was added to excess dilute hydrochloric acid.

$$Zn + 2HCl \rightarrow ZnCl_2 + H_2$$

Calculate:

a. the maximum mass of zinc chloride, $ZnCl_2$, produced

b. the maximum mass of hydrogen produced.

1. The box shows the formulae of some ions and molecules.

Al^{3+} Ca^{2+} CH_4 Cl^- CO_2 CO_3^{2-} H^+ H_2O NO_3^- SO_2 SO_4^{2-}

Answer the following questions using the formulae from the box.

a. Select **two anions**. _____

b. Select **two cations**. _____

c. Select **two** molecules. _____

d. Select **two** ions that will move to the positively charged **electrode**. _____

e. Write down the formula of calcium carbonate. _____

f. Write down the formula of aluminium chloride. _____

2. State what is meant by the following words:

a. electrolysis _____

b. electrolyte _____

c. anode _____

d. cathode _____

3. Sodium chloride is an ionic compound. Give a reason why solid sodium chloride does not conduct electricity.

_____

4. The state symbols (aq) and (l) can be used alongside the formulae of ions when they are electrolysed. Describe the meaning of each of these state symbols.

(aq) _____   (l) _____

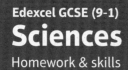

5. Explain why it is important to use a direct current (d.c.) for electrolysis and not an alternating current (a.c.).

_____

_____

_____

_____

_____

_____

_____

_____

Edexcel GCSE (9-1)
Sciences
Homework & skills
CC11a Reactivity
**CC11 Obtaining and
Using Metals**

1. The general reactions of metals that react with water and acids are:

    metal + water → metal hydroxide + hydrogen

    metal + acid → salt + hydrogen

2. A metal will displace metals below it in the **reactivity series** from their compounds.

3. Some useful formulae: CaO, $Ca(OH)_2$, Cl^-, Mg^{2+}, $MgCl_2$, $MgSO_4$, $ZnCl_2$, ZnO, $ZnSO_4$

1. Describe what is seen when a small piece of sodium is added to water.

_____

_____

2. Write word equations for the following reactions.

a. potassium with water

_____

b. iron with sulfuric acid

_____

3. Write balanced equations for the following reactions.

a. calcium with water

_____

b. zinc with hydrochloric acid

_____

4. Magnesium reacts with copper chloride solution to form magnesium chloride solution and copper.

a. Give the formula of magnesium chloride. _____

b. Give the state symbol for magnesium chloride solution. _____

c. State what you would see during this reaction. _____

_____

5. Predict whether each of these reactions will take place. Either complete the balanced equation or write 'no reaction'.

a. $Ca + FeO →$ _____

b. $Cu + ZnO →$ _____

c. $Zn + FeO →$ _____

d. $Zn + CuSO_4 →$ _____

e. $Mg + ZnCl_2 →$ _____

f. $Zn + CuCl_2 →$ _____

g. $Cu + Ca(NO_3)_2 →$ _____

1. Complete the following sentences.

a. When carbon forms carbon dioxide it is oxidised, because _____

b. When lead oxide forms lead it is reduced, because _____

2. A mixture of copper oxide and carbon powder was heated in the apparatus shown. A gas was produced and it was bubbled into limewater.

a. The limewater turned milky. Identify the gas produced in this reaction.

_____

_____

b. A brown solid formed in the test tube X. Identify the brown solid.

_____

_____

copper oxide +
carbon powder

test tube X

heat

limewater

c. Write the word equation for the reaction.

_____

d. In this reaction a substance is reduced. Explain which substance is reduced.

_____

e. The mass of test tube X and its contents was measured before and after heating. There was a change in mass. Explain why the total mass of the test tube and contents changes during the reaction.

_____

_____

3. Iron corrodes when it is left in moist air. The list shows iron and three other metals in **reactivity series** order, with the most reactive metal at the top.

most reactive   ↑   magnesium

iron

lead

least reactive   silver

Explain which metal or metals in the list will corrode faster than iron.

_____

_____

4. Iron nails **rust** quickly. Give a reason why coating the iron nails with zinc prevents the nails from rusting.

_____

There is more aluminium in the Earth's crust than iron. However, aluminium is more expensive. This is because aluminium has to be **extracted** by the electrolysis of its molten **ore**, rather than heating its ore with carbon.

Table 1 Metal reserves are running out.

Metal	Years left if used at current rate
aluminium	25
copper	59
gold	12
iron	287

Table 2 We have to consider the concentration of the metal in the ore.

Metal	Concentration in ore needed to make extraction worthwhile
aluminium	32%
copper	0.5%
gold	0.0014%
iron	25%

Recycling metals has many advantages. The first step in recycling involves taking the metals to a recycling plant, sorting them and cleaning them. Each type of metal can then be melted down and made into new items.

1. Using data from table 1, state which metal is likely to run out first. _____

2. **a.** Which method of extraction is used to obtain:

    i aluminium _____

    ii iron? _____

   b. Suggest why the way aluminium is extracted makes it a more expensive metal than iron.

   _____

3. Look at the data for iron and copper in tables 1 and 2.

   a. Which of these two metals is likely to run out first? _____

   b. Suggest why manufacturers only extract iron when at least 25 per cent of the ore is iron, while they extract copper that is only 0.5 per cent of the ore.

   _____

   _____

4. State **two** advantages of recycling metals.

   _____

   _____

5. State a disadvantage of recycling some metals.

   _____

6. A manufacturer is trying to decide whether to make a drinks container from aluminium or glass.

   a. Complete the four stages in a life cycle assessment.

   Obtaining and processing _____ , manufacturing and _____ the

   product, _____ the product, disposing of _____ .

   b. State an advantage of glass bottles compared with aluminium cans for drinks containers.

   _____

   c. State an advantage of aluminium cans compared with glass bottles for drinks containers.

   _____

1. The diagram shows the **reversible reaction** involving the decomposition of ammonium chloride to form ammonia and hydrogen chloride.

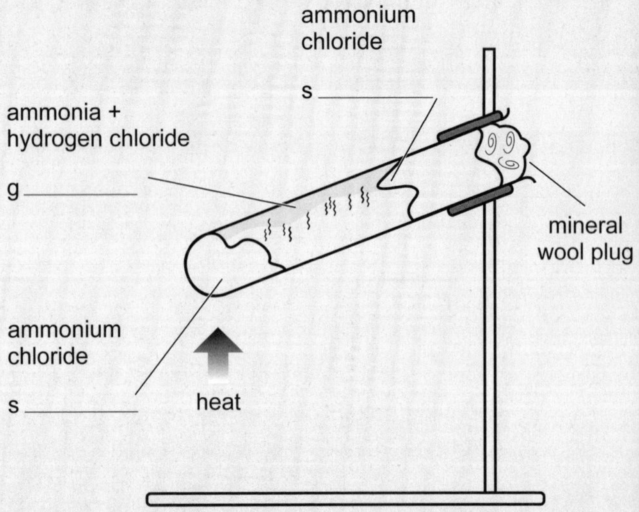

a. Complete the labels on the diagram.

ammonium chloride

s _____

b. Complete the word and balanced equations below for the reaction involved.

ammonia + hydrogen chloride

g _____

ammonium chloride $\rightleftharpoons$

_____ + hydrogen chloride

$NH_4Cl(s)$ $\rightleftharpoons$

$NH_3(g)$ + _____ (g)

mineral wool plug

ammonium chloride

s _____   heat

c. The reaction is said to achieve a **dynamic equilibrium**. Define this term.

_____

_____

_____

_____

d. Explain why equilibrium will only be achieved if the reaction is carried out in a sealed container.

_____

_____

_____

2. Ammonia is an important product of the chemical industry. It is formed from nitrogen and hydrogen:

_____ $H_2(g)$ + _____ $N_2(g)$ $\rightleftharpoons$ _____ $NH_3(g)$

a. Add numbers to balance the chemical equation.

b. What does the sign, $\rightleftharpoons$, tell us about the reaction?

_____

c. Write a word equation for this reaction.

_____

d. State the temperature, pressure and catalyst used in the industrial process for producing ammonia.

_____

_____

_____

_____

Sciences **CC13a** Group 1

Homework & skills

1. Write the names of **groups** 1, 7 and 0 in the **periodic table** below and add the symbols for the first three elements in group 1.

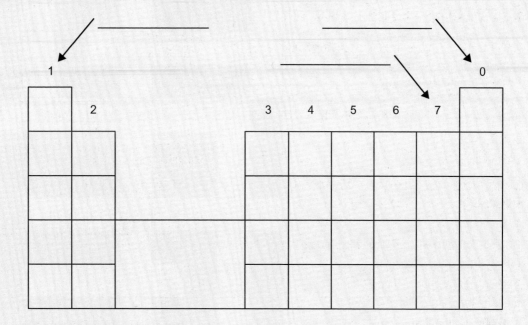

2. The diagrams opposite show two **alkali metals** reacting with water.

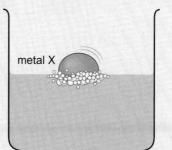

a. Which metal is more reactive? _____

b. If metal X is sodium, suggest a name for metal Y. _____

c. Name a less reactive alkali metal than X and Y.

_____

d. Complete the word and balanced equations for sodium reacting with water. *Hint:* you can use the examples at the bottom of the page if you need to.

sodium + _____ → _____ + _____

____Na + _____ → _____ + _____

3. Some data on four metals is shown in the table below. Identify the alkali metal and explain your choice.

Metal	Melting point (°C)	Boiling point (°C)	Soft or hard?
P	1535	2750	hard
Q	98	883	soft
R	1083	2567	hard
S	660	2467	hard

_____

_____

_____

These examples will help you to answer question **2d**.

word equation: lithium + water   → lithium hydroxide + hydrogen

balanced equation: $2Li (s)$ + $2H_2O (l)$ → $2LiOH (aq)$ + $H_2 (g)$

1. Complete the crossword.

Across

4 See 3 down (6)

5 A compound of fluorine (8)

7 Type of bonding holding **halogen** molecules together (8)

8 Number of atoms in a halogen molecule (3)

9 The colour of bromine (5)

10 A pale green gas at room temperature (8)

Down

1 See 2 down

2 and 1 Formed when hydrogen chloride dissolves in water (12) & (4)

3 down and 4 across The product of reacting lead and iodine (4) & (6)

5 The first element in group 7 (8)

6 The only halogen that is a liquid at room temperature (7)

2. Look at the table opposite.

a. Describe the trend in the melting point of the halogens down the group.

b. Suggest what the missing information in the table could be. Add your answers to the table.

Halogen	State at 20 °C	Melting point (°C)
fluorine		
chlorine	gas	−101
bromine	liquid	−7
iodine	solid	114

3. Write a word equation for the reaction of sodium and iodine.

4. Write a balanced equation with state symbols for the reaction between hydrogen, H_2, and fluorine, F_2.

5. Zinc foil bursts into flames when it reacts with chlorine. It glows brightly and produces sparks with bromine, and glows red with iodine.

Suggest what the reaction between zinc foil and astatine would look like and explain how you predicted its reactivity. Name the product formed in the reaction.

 6. Describe the chemical test for chlorine gas.

1. a. Add electrons to the diagrams and complete the electronic configurations and the sentences below.

helium (_____)	**neon (_____ . _____)**	**argon (_____ . _____ . _____)**
He atomic number = 2	Ne atomic number = 10	Ar atomic number = 18

b. The group 0 elements all have an electronic configuration that includes a c_____ outer shell of electrons.

c. Most group 0 elements, called the n_____ gases, have an outer shell of _____ electrons, except helium which has _____ electrons in its outer shell.

d. This is a very stable arrangement of electrons and this makes the **noble gases** i_____, which means they do not r_____ easily with other substances.

2. Link the uses of group 0 elements listed below with the descriptions of properties that make each element suitable for that use. Each use can be linked to more than one property.

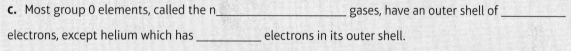

Argon is used in welding to stop the hot metal reacting with oxygen in the air.	very reactive
	non-flammable
Helium is used in airships and party balloons.	high density gas
Argon is used to put out fires in computer rooms.	low density gas
Argon is used inside filament lamps to stop the hot filament reacting with oxygen.	brightly coloured
	relatively **inert**

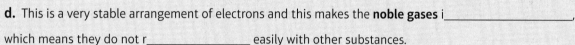

3. The boiling points of some group 0 elements are given below, and their atomic numbers are shown in brackets.

helium (2) –269 °C   argon (18) –186 °C

krypton (36) –153 °C   xenon (54) –108 °C

a. Draw a scatter graph using the axes opposite.

b. Predict the boiling point of neon (atomic number 10):

_____ °C

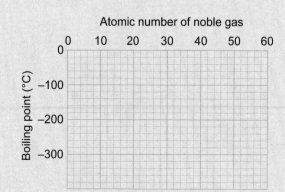

1. The graph shows the results obtained when investigating the reaction between nickel carbonate and hydrochloric acid at different temperatures.

a. Which graph shows the reaction carried out at the higher temperature?

_____

b. Explain your answer.

_____

_____

_____

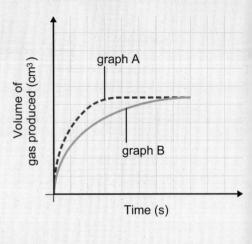

2. Complete the word equation for the reaction between nickel carbonate and hydrochloric acid.

nickel carbonate + hydrochloric acid → _____ _____ + carbon dioxide + _____

3. Use the box opposite to draw a labelled diagram of how you would set up apparatus for the investigation in question **1**. You need to measure the volume of gas produced at different temperatures.

4. In this experiment, the dependent variable is the _____ of gas produced and the independent variable is the _____.

5. Two control variables are the _____ of acid and the size of the solid lumps of _____.

6. Look at the graph at the top of the page.

Explain why both lines on the graph become less steep with time and eventually level off.

_____

_____

1. Draw lines to link the start and end of each of the sentences below to make correct statements.

Catalysts are used to ...	... the activation energy.
Catalysts allow chemical reactions to ...	... have enough energy needed for reaction.
Catalysts can be used again and again ...	... happen at lower temperatures.
Catalysts work by lowering ...	... speed up chemical reactions.
Using a catalyst means more molecules ...	... because they are not used up.

2. The graph below shows the **reaction profile** for an exothermic reaction with a catalyst added.

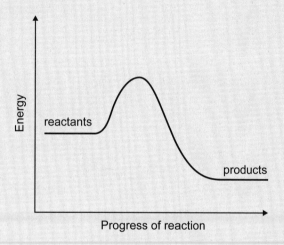

a. Draw an arrowed line to indicate the activation energy of the catalysed reaction and label it.

b. Draw a dotted line on the graph to represent the reaction energy profile for the same reaction without the catalyst present.

c. Complete the following sentence to explain why the reaction is slower without a catalyst present.

Without the catalyst the activation energy is _____, so _____ reactant

particles have enough _____ to react when they collide. This means fewer collisions result in

a _____, and the overall rate of reaction is _____.

3. Choose one word or phrase from the box below to fit each of the following descriptions.

active site	catalyst	**enzyme**	**substrate**	**denatured**	**protein**

a. a protein that acts as a biological catalyst: _____

b. part of an enzyme molecule that fits the reacting molecules: _____

c. a molecule that has changed shape due to changes in temperature or pH: _____

d. the substance that is changed by a biological catalyst: _____

Edexcel GCSE (9-1)
Sciences
Homework & skills

CC15a Exothermic and
endothermic reactions

**CC15 Heat Energy
Changes in Chemical
Reactions**

1. Which row in the table (A, B, C or D) correctly describes what happens during reactions in solution?

	Exothermic reactions		Endothermic reactions	
A	heat energy taken in	temperature increases	heat energy given out	temperature decreases
B	heat energy given out	temperature decreases	heat energy taken in	temperature increases
C	heat energy taken in	temperature decreases	heat energy given out	temperature increases
D	heat energy given out	temperature increases	heat energy taken in	temperature decreases

Answer _____

2. Zinc powder reacts with copper sulfate solution:

$Zn(s) + CuSO_4(aq) \rightarrow ZnSO_4(aq) + Cu(s)$

A student uses the apparatus shown in the diagram to investigate temperature changes in this reaction.

The starting temperature of the copper sulfate solution was 18.7 °C. The maximum temperature reached after the zinc was added was 43.3 °C.

a. Calculate the change in temperature during the experiment.

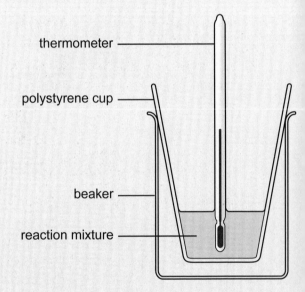

thermometer ——

polystyrene cup ——

beaker ——

reaction mixture ——

_____

_____

_____

b. Explain, using your answer to part **a**, whether the reaction was **exothermic** or **endothermic**.

_____

_____

c. The student stirred the mixture continually with the thermometer. Suggest **two** reasons for this.

_____

_____

_____

d. State and explain **one** improvement to the apparatus that would produce more accurate results.

_____

_____

_____

3. Reactions between an acid and an alkali are exothermic. Name a type of reaction in solution that can be exothermic *or* endothermic, depending on the substances used.

_____

_____

4. When a salt dissolves in water, the change can be exothermic *or* endothermic, depending on the salt used. A student dissolves 1 g of sodium chloride in 250 cm³ of water. Suggest a reason why he does not observe a temperature change, even though the dissolving of sodium chloride is known to be an endothermic process.

_____

_____

Edexcel GCSE (9-1)
Sciences
Homework & skills

CC16a Hydrocarbons in crude oil
and natural gas

CC16 Fuels

1. The diagrams show the structures of four different compounds.

compound 1   compound 2   compound 3   compound 4

a. Identify which of these compounds (1, 2, 3 and 4) are **hydrocarbons**.

_____

b. Explain your answer to part **a**.

_____

2. **Natural gas** and **crude oil** are mixtures of hydrocarbons.

a. Complete the table by placing a tick (✔) in each correct box to show the physical state or states of their individual hydrocarbon components at room temperature.

	State of individual components at room temperature		
	solid	liquid	gas
natural gas			
crude oil			

b. Describe the arrangements of the carbon atoms in the hydrocarbon molecules found in crude oil.

_____

3. Crude oil is described as a **finite resource**. Explain what this means.

_____

_____

4. Ethene is a substance obtained from crude oil. It is used to make **petrochemicals** such as poly(ethene).

a. State what is meant by a petrochemical.

_____

b. Why is ethene described as a **feedstock** for making industrial substances?

_____

5. Kerosene is a **fossil fuel** obtained from crude oil.

a. Name **two** other fossil fuels obtained from crude oil._____

b. Name the main fossil fuel found in natural gas. _____

c. The fossil fuels are being used up faster than they can be replaced. Give the word that describes resources like these.

_____

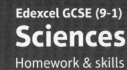

Sciences **CC16b** Fractional distillation of crude oil
Homework & skills

1. Crude oil **fractions** have different uses.

a. Complete the table by writing the missing names and uses of each fraction into the correct boxes.

Name of fraction	Use of fraction
	domestic heating and cooking
petrol	
kerosene	
	fuel for some trains
	fuel for some power stations
	surfacing roads and roofs

b. State one other use for the fraction used for:

i **fuel** for some trains

_____

ii fuel for some power stations.

_____

2. During the **fractional distillation** of crude oil, petrol vapours **condense** higher up the **fractionating column** than kerosene vapours do.

a. Describe the change of state that happens during condensation.

_____

b. State and explain which fraction (petrol or kerosene):

i has the lower boiling point _____

_____

ii contains the smaller hydrocarbon molecules _____

_____

iii **ignites** more easily _____

_____

iv has the higher **viscosity**. _____

3. Explain how crude oil is separated into simpler, more useful mixtures by fractional distillation. In your answer, include just the essential processes.

_____

_____

_____

1. There are several different **homologous series**. Complete the table by placing a tick (✔) in each correct box to show the **general** features of all homologous series.

Feature	✔
Their compounds all have the same physical properties.	
Their compounds all have similar chemical properties.	
Their compounds all have the same **general formula**.	
Their molecules all contain ionic bonds.	

2. The **alkanes** form an homologous series. The diagram shows the **structural formula** of butane.

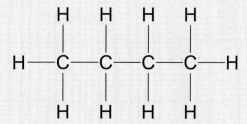

a. State the number of:

   i   carbon atoms in a molecule of butane

_____

_____

   ii   hydrogen atoms in a molecule of butane.

_____

b. Use your answers to part **a** to write the **molecular formula** for butane.

_____

c. Pentane, C_5H_{12}, is the next alkane in the alkane homologous series.

   i   Draw the structural formula of pentane in the box.

   ii   Describe **two** differences between the structural formulae of butane and pentane.

_____

_____

d. Use your answers to parts **b** and **c** to describe how the molecular formulae of pentane and butane differ from each other.

_____

3. The different fractions obtained from crude oil contain compounds that are mostly alkanes.

a. Explain why alkanes can be described as **hydrocarbons**.

_____

b. The different alkanes in crude oil are separated into fractions by fractional distillation.

   i   Name the physical property that allows a mixture of alkanes to be separated by this method.

_____

   ii   Describe how the physical property named in part **i** changes in the alkane homologous series.

_____

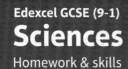

1. A Bunsen burner burns natural gas. Natural gas is a mixture of methane (CH_4) and other hydrocarbons. Complete the table by placing a tick (✔) in one box in each row to describe what happens when a Bunsen burner is used.

	Complete combustion	Incomplete combustion
Blue flame		
Luminous orange flame		
Hottest flame		
Air hole closed		

2. a. Name the products formed during the **complete combustion** of methane.

_____

b. Write a word equation for the complete combustion of methane.

_____

c. Describe **two** ways in which energy is transferred to the surroundings during the **combustion** of methane.

1 _____

2 _____

3. The **incomplete combustion** of petrol produces carbon and **carbon monoxide**.

a. Describe how incomplete combustion of petrol, rather than complete combustion, can happen.

_____

b. Describe **two** ways you can tell that carbon is released during the incomplete combustion of petrol.

1 _____

2 _____

c. Describe **two** problems caused by carbon released during incomplete combustion.

1 _____

2 _____

d. Explain why the incomplete combustion of petrol produces carbon monoxide.

_____

4. Carbon monoxide is a colourless and odourless **toxic** gas.

a. Explain why electronic carbon monoxide detectors are used near to gas appliances.

_____

b. Explain how carbon monoxide behaves as a toxic gas. You do not need to describe any symptoms of carbon monoxide poisoning in your answer.

_____

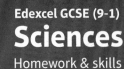

Sciences **CC16f** Breaking down hydrocarbons
Homework & skills

1. Alkanes and **alkenes** are two homologous series. Complete the table by placing a tick (✔) in each correct box.

	Alkanes	Alkenes
Saturated compounds		
Unsaturated compounds		

2. In general, which are more useful as fuels, alkanes with shorter or longer carbon chains?

_____

3. Which hydrocarbons are useful for making polymers, alkanes or alkenes?

_____

4. Alkenes can be obtained by **cracking** some crude oil fractions. Explain what is meant by 'cracking'.

_____

_____

_____

_____

5. The table shows the percentage composition of a crude oil, and the percentage demand for each fraction.

Use the data in the table to help you explain why cracking is necessary.

Fraction	Composition (%)	Demand (%)
gases	3	6
petrol	10	27
kerosene	11	19
diesel oil	15	23
fuel oil	49	21
bitumen	12	4

_____

_____

_____

_____

6. **a.** Describe **one** advantage of using hydrogen, rather than petrol, as a vehicle fuel.

_____

_____

b. Describe **two** disadvantages of using hydrogen, rather than petrol, as a vehicle fuel.

1 _____

2 _____

1. Draw lines to link what the Earth's early **atmosphere** is thought to have contained with the evidence.

What the Earth's early atmosphere is thought to have contained	Evidence for what the Earth's early atmosphere contained
Water vapour	Volcanoes on rocky planets in the Solar System are thought to release carbon dioxide and there was a lot of **volcanic activity** on the early Earth.
Small amounts of methane and ammonia	The earliest fossils of photosynthetic organisms are about 1 billion years younger than the Earth.
A large amount of carbon dioxide	Volcanoes on Earth release small amounts of methane and ammonia.
Little or no oxygen	Water vapour condenses to form liquid when it cools, which would form the large oceans we see today.

2. Use words from the box to complete the sentences about how oceans were formed. You may use each word once, more than once or not at all.

4	500	atmosphere	cold	condense	cooled	crust	earthquakes
evaporate	gas	hot	liquid	the Sun	vapour	volcanoes	warmed

For the first _____ million years of the Earth's history, there were no oceans because the Earth

was too _____. The Earth's _____ contained a lot of water _____,

released by _____. About _____ billion years ago, the Earth _____.

This allowed the water _____ to _____ to form _____ water, which then

formed the seas and oceans.

3. The formula H_2O tells you that in water the ratio of hydrogen to oxygen is 2 : 1. Or, you can state this the other way around: the ratio of oxygen to hydrogen is 1 : 2.

a. What is the ratio of oxygen to iron in the compound Fe_3O_4? _____

b. What is the ratio of oxygen to iron in the compound Fe_2O_3? _____

c. If you have 6 atoms of iron in a tiny quantity of Fe_3O_4, how many oxygen atoms will there be?

_____

d. If you have 6 atoms of iron in a tiny quantity of Fe_2O_3, how many oxygen atoms will there be?

_____

e. Give the reason why Fe_2O_3 is more likely to form in the presence of greater concentrations of oxygen.

_____

Scientists think that small quantities of oxygen were first produced on Earth about 3.5 billion years ago. Larger and larger quantities then started to be made.

f. Which of the iron compounds, Fe_3O_4 and Fe_2O_3, would you expect to find in earlier rocks? Explain your answer.

_____

g. What do scientists think was the reason for oxygen being produced 3.5 billion years ago?

_____

1. The diagram shows how the Earth is kept warm by its atmosphere.

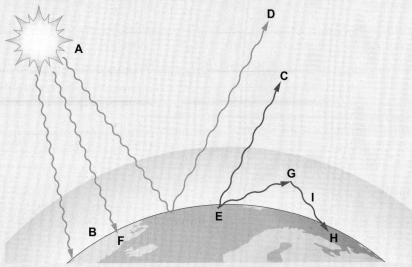

The labels for the diagram are shown below. Write the letters from the diagram next to the correct labels.

Energy is transferred from the Sun.	Some of the energy emitted by the Earth is **absorbed** by **greenhouse gases**.	Some emitted energy is transferred to space.
Some of the energy that reaches the Earth's surface is reflected back into space.	When energy is reemitted it can be transferred back to the Earth.	Most of the energy is absorbed by the Earth's surface, increasing its temperature.
The warm Earth **emits** energy.	Greenhouse gases re-emit the energy that they absorb.	Energy from the Sun reaches the Earth's surface.

2. Draw lines to match each term with its meaning.

global warming   alterations to global weather patterns

climate change   atmospheric gases trapping energy

greenhouse effect   a gradual increase in the temperature of the Earth's atmosphere

3. Scientists think that carbon dioxide is a greenhouse gas.

a. Evidence to support this includes a **correlation** between changes in carbon dioxide levels and changes in temperature, in the past 200 000 years. What is a 'correlation'?

_____

b. Give the names of **two** other greenhouse gases.

_____

c. Describe **one** further piece of evidence to support the idea that carbon dioxide is a greenhouse gas.

_____

_____

d. Give a reason why measurements of global temperatures today provide better evidence than temperature measurements made 200 years ago.

_____

_____

1. Complete the paragraph below, using words from the box. You may use each word once, more than once or not at all.

atmosphere	cattle	climate change	energy	fall	fossil	greenhouse
	infrared	landfill	methane	rise	space	surface

Human activities release _____ gases, which trap heat in the _____. Two of these gases are carbon

dioxide and _____. These gases absorb _____ that is being transferred by _____ radiation

from the surface of the Earth. This stops the energy escaping into _____, and so causes a _____ in

global temperatures.

Carbon dioxide is released when _____ fuels are burnt. Methane is produced by livestock, especially

_____. Methane is also released from _____ sites.

2. The list shows some causes and effects of climate change. Circle only the effects of climate change.

increase in droughts in some areas	increase in pH of the oceans	increase in floods
global warming	decrease in greenhouse gas levels	increase in violent storms

3. To reduce global warming some engineers have suggested reflecting sunlight back into space.

a. Explain how this idea will work.

_____

b. Describe **two** problems that need to be overcome if this idea is to be used.

_____

_____

4. Dams that hold back large volumes of water in reservoirs have benefits and risks. Place one tick (✔) in each row showing whether each feature describes a benefit or a risk of harm.

Feature	Benefit?	Risk?
water storage for crop irrigation	☐	☐
habitat destruction	☐	☐
can generate electricity (hydroelectric power)	☐	☐
can trap heavy rainfall	☐	☐
provide recreation areas for people	☐	☐
can burst if not built strongly	☐	☐
stops fish migrating up rivers	☐	☐

Sciences

CP1a Vectors and scalars

Homework & skills

1. Al and Ben started at A and travelled north to B. Then they turned east and went to C, then south to D and then travelled west back to A. The **distance** in a straight line between A and C is 500 m.

Complete the sentences below.

a. When Al and Ben were at point B they had travelled a

distance of _____ metres.

Their **displacement** from point A was

_____ metres north.

b. When they were at point C they had travelled a

distance of _____ metres from point A.

Their displacement from point A was _____

metres at a bearing of 53° east of north.

c. When they were at point D they had travelled a total of _____ metres from point A.

Their displacement from point A was _____ metres (north/south/east/west).

d. When they were back at point A they had travelled a total of _____ metres.

Their displacement from point A was _____ metres.

2. Al walked at a constant **speed** of 1.5 m/s. Ben jogged at 3 m/s. Complete the table to show their **velocities** for each part of their journey.

	Al's velocity	Ben's velocity
A to B	1.5 m/s north	
B to C		
C to D		
D to A		3 m/s west

3. The table below shows some things that can be measured. Tick the boxes to show if each one is a **vector** or a **scalar quantity**.

Quantity	Vector	Scalar
a. force		
b. weight		
c. mass		
d. acceleration		
e. displacement		
f. speed		
g. distance		
h. energy		

Sciences **CP1b** Distance/time graphs
Homework & skills

This is a **distance/time graph** for a cyclist travelling along a road.

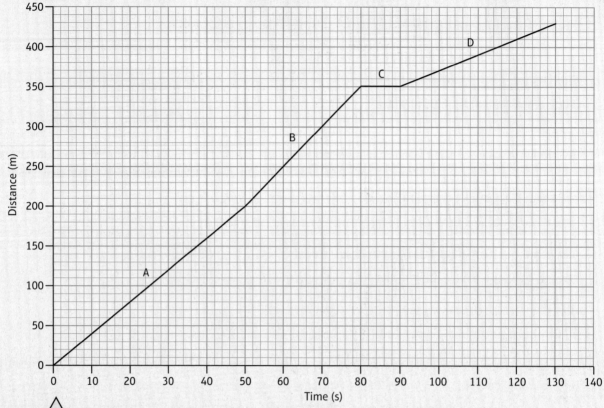

This triangle can help you rearrange the equation for speed. Cover up the quantity you want to calculate, then write what you can see on the right of your = sign.

distance / (speed × time)

1. a. Which section of the graph shows where the cyclist waited at a junction? _____

b. For how long did the cyclist wait? _____

2. a. Which section of the graph shows where the cyclist was travelling the fastest? _____

b. How can you tell from the graph that the speed was greatest here? _____

3. a. How far did the cyclist travel in the first 50 s? _____

b. Calculate the speed in the first 50 s.

speed = _____ m/s

4. Part of the journey was uphill. Explain which part of the graph is likely to show this part of the journey.

_____

5. A cheetah can run for a short time at 31 m/s (70 mph). How far can it travel in 19 s?

distance = _____ m

6. A tortoise can crawl at a top speed of 0.2 m/s. How long will it take the tortoise to travel 15 m?

time = _____ s

Sciences   **CP1d** Velocity/time graphs
Homework & skills

1. This is a **velocity/time graph** for a horse and rider travelling along a straight track. (A gallop is faster than a trot.)

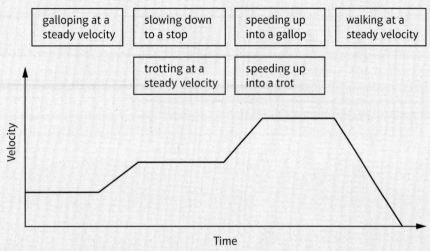

| galloping at a steady velocity | slowing down to a stop | speeding up into a gallop | walking at a steady velocity |

| trotting at a steady velocity | speeding up into a trot |

a. Draw a line from each label to the correct part of the graph.

b. Which acceleration was greater? Tick the correct answer.

☐ speeding up into a gallop   ☐ speeding up into a trot

Explain your choice. _____

_____

2. a. Calculate the acceleration in part C of this graph.

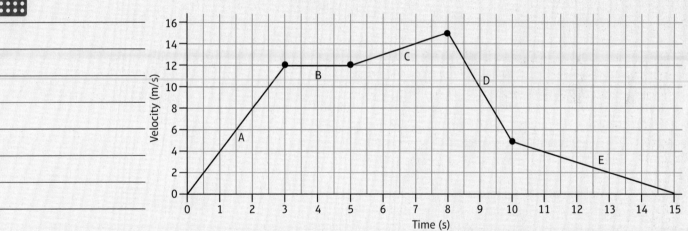

b. Calculate the acceleration in part D of the graph.

c. Calculate the distance travelled in the first five seconds. (*Hint*: Calculate the distance travelled in part A by working out the area of a triangle. Calculate the distance travelled in part B by working out the area of a rectangle.)

| gradient = $\dfrac{\text{vertical difference}}{\text{horizontal difference}}$ | area of rectangle = base × height | area of triangle = 0.5 × base × height |

1. A force is a **vector quantity**. Tick the box next to the best description of what this means.

☐ A force can be represented using an arrow.

☐ A force has both a size and a direction.

☐ Forces always act in the same direction.

☐ Forces can be pushes or pulls.

2. The arrow on the right represents a force.

Draw another arrow underneath it that represents a larger force acting in the opposite direction.

3. The arrows represent forces on a car.

Draw an arrow underneath that represents the **resultant force** on the car.

friction and drag   forwards force from engine

4. The drawing shows a sailing boat.

a. The weight and upthrust forces are the same size as each other. Draw labelled force arrows on the diagram to show these two forces.

b. There is a forwards force from the sails acting on the boat. Draw a labelled force arrow to show this force.

c. There is also a drag force on the boat. This force is smaller than the force from the sails. Draw a labelled force arrow to show this force.

5. The upthrust force on the boat in question **4** is 50 000 N and its weight is 50 000 N. Circle the words or phrases that describe the vertical forces on the boat.

balanced   unbalanced   non-zero resultant   zero resultant
resultant acts upwards   resultant acts downwards

6. The force from the sails is larger than the drag forces on the boat. Circle the words or phrases that describe the horizontal forces on the boat.

balanced   unbalanced   non-zero resultant   zero resultant
resultant acts forwards   resultant acts backwards

1. Fill in the gaps in these sentences using words from the box below. You can use each word once, more than once or not at all.

force	gravitational	gravity	kilograms	mass	matter
metres	N/kg	newtons	size	strength	volume	weight

The **weight** of an object is the _____ of _____ pulling down on it. It is measured

in _____ .

Weight depends on the _____ of an object and on the _____ of gravity. On Earth, the

_____ field strength is approximately 10 _____ .

The **mass** of an object is a way of measuring the amount of _____ in it. Mass is measured in

_____ .

2. The formula triangle helps you to rearrange the formula for calculating weight.

a. What does *W* stand for? _____

b. What does *m* stand for? _____

c. What does *g* stand for? _____

d. Write down the formula for calculating weight:

weight (in N) = _____ (in kg) × _____ (in N/kg)

3. The drawing shows a hot air balloon. The mass of the balloon is 3000 kg.

a. Calculate the weight of the balloon.

34 000 N

Weight of balloon = _____

b. Draw an arrow on the balloon to represent this force.

c. What is the resultant force on the balloon?

resultant force = _____ N (upwards/downwards)

d. What will happen to the velocity of the balloon?

Hot air balloons sometimes carry ballast. Ballast provides extra mass that can be thrown out of the balloon if it needs to be made lighter.

4. At the end of a flight, the balloon in question **3** has a weight of 28 000 N. Calculate the mass of the balloon at this time.

Mass of balloon = _____

Sciences
CP2d Newton's Second Law

Homework & skills

1. What are the resultant forces acting on these objects?

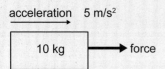

acceleration 5 m/s²

10 kg → force

$\dfrac{F}{m \times a}$

a. An object of mass 10 kg accelerating at 5 m/s².

_____ N

b. mass 15 kg, acceleration 5 m/s² _____ N

c. mass 20 kg, acceleration 8 m/s² _____ N

d. mass 16 kg, acceleration 10 m/s² _____ N

2. Complete these sentences using the words 'greater' or 'smaller'.

a. For objects of the same mass, a larger resultant force will give a _____ acceleration.

b. For the same resultant force, the more massive the object, the _____ the acceleration.

3. For each of the following diagrams:

- calculate the resultant force
- give the direction of the resultant force
- calculate the acceleration of the object.

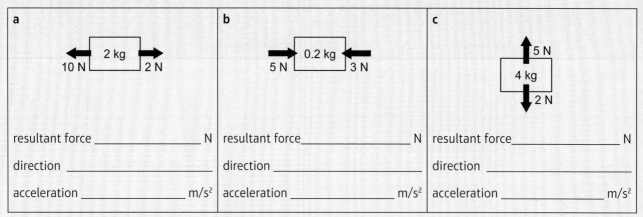

a

10 N ← 2 kg → 2 N

resultant force _____ N

direction _____

acceleration _____ m/s²

b

5 N → 0.2 kg ← 3 N

resultant force _____ N

direction _____

acceleration _____ m/s²

c

↑ 5 N

4 kg

↓ 2 N

resultant force _____ N

direction _____

acceleration _____ m/s²

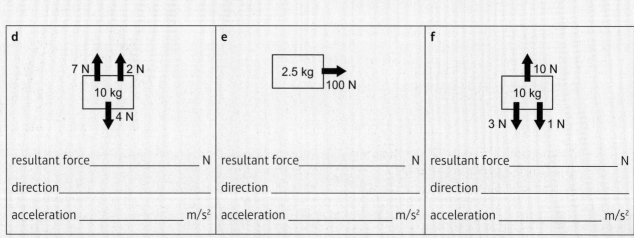

d

7 N ↑ ↑ 2 N

10 kg

↓ 4 N

resultant force _____ N

direction _____

acceleration _____ m/s²

e

2.5 kg → 100 N

resultant force _____ N

direction _____

acceleration _____ m/s²

f

↑ 10 N

10 kg

3 N ↓ ↓ 1 N

resultant force _____ N

direction _____

acceleration _____ m/s²

Sciences **CP2e** Newton's Third Law
Homework & skills

1. This helium balloon is tied to a brick to stop the balloon from floating away. Some of the forces acting are listed below.

pull of string on the brick = 0.5 N   pull of string on the balloon = 0.5 N

pull of balloon on the string = 0.5 N   pull of brick on the string= 0.5 N

weight of the balloon = 0.5 N   upthrust from the air = 1.0 N

a. In the list above there are two pairs of action and reaction forces. Use lines to join the forces in each pair.

b. Which force(s) pull the balloon down?

_____

c. Which force(s) push the balloon up?

_____

_____

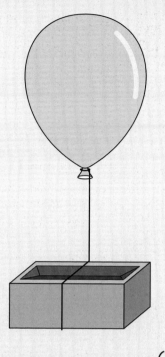

2. Astronauts train for space walks in a tank of water.
The floating feeling in water is similar to the feeling in space.

Complete the following sentences using words from the box. You do not need all the words.

The upwards force is _____

from the water. The downwards force is the astronaut's

_____. The two forces are

_____ forces because they are acting on

_____ .

action–reaction	balanced
different objects	the same object
upthrust	weight

3. Two boys are pushing on each other. They are not moving.

a. Draw arrows on Al to show the action–reaction pair of forces at his feet.

b. Force W is 40 N. What force is Ben putting on Al?

_____

c. What kind of force causes forces Y and Z?

_____

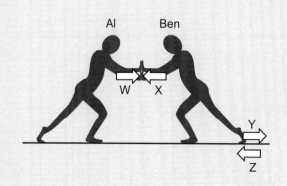

d. Ben is not moving, so the forces on him must be balanced. Which **two** of the forces on the diagram (W, X, Y, Z) form a pair of **balanced forces** on Ben?

_____

1. Tick the boxes to show if each of these statements is true or false. For the false statements, write a corrected version underneath. For the true statements, try to explain why they are true.

	True	False

a.　The faster a car goes, the longer its **stopping distance** will be.　　☐　☐

_____

b.　If a driver is tired, the **thinking distance** will be less.　　☐　☐

_____

c.　If a driver has taken drugs, the thinking distance will be increased.　　☐　☐

_____

d.　If the road is wet, the thinking distance will be longer.　　☐　☐

_____

e.　A car with four passengers will have a shorter **braking distance** than a car with one passenger.　　☐　☐

_____

f.　Worn tyres will make the braking distance longer.　　☐　☐

_____

2. Road safety advice suggests that people should drive more slowly when it is raining than when it is dry. Complete the following sentences to explain this advice. Use words from the box – you can use each word once, more than once or not at all.

better	braking	closer to	decrease	further from	increase
longer	reacting	shorter	stopping	thinking	worse

If there is a hazard on the road ahead, a car travels a certain distance while the driver is _____

to the danger (the _____ distance) and while the car is slowing down (the _____

distance). The total distance is called the _____ distance. If the hazard is _____

the car than the stopping distance, the car will not stop in time and the driver will hit it.

If it is raining the driver cannot see as far as on a dry day. If they slow down their stopping distance gets

_____ , and so they have a _____ chance of being able to stop before they

hit something.

Rain on the road will also _____ the friction between the tyres and the road. This will _____

the braking distance, so the driver also needs to slow down to compensate for this.

3. At 25 m/s, a car's stopping distance will be longer than when the car travels at 15 m/s. Explain why.

_____

_____

_____

1. Most cars use energy stored in petrol or diesel.

a. What is the name for the way energy is stored in petrol? _____

b. What is the name for the energy stored in the moving car? _____

c. What forms of wasted energy does a car's engine transfer? _____

d. Explain what happens to the energy stored in the moving car when the driver applies the brakes to stop the car. Use all the words in the box in your answer.

brakes	by heating	forces	friction
surroundings	temperature	transferred	

_____

_____

2. What is the name for the way energy is stored in Jenny when:

a. she is at the top of the slide _____

b. she reaches the bottom of the slide?

_____

3. A ball bounces when it hits the ground.

a. Complete the diagram to show the energy stores and transfers as the ball falls to the ground.

energy stored in ball before it is dropped (_____ _____ energy)	energy transferred by forces →	energy stored in moving ball just before it hits the ground (_____ energy)	energy transferred by forces →	energy stored in squashed ball as it hits the ground (_____ _____ energy)

b. Describe the energy transfers and stores as the ball moves upwards to the top of the next bounce.

_____

4. The diagram shows energy transfers in a television. The TV transfers 10 J of energy by light each second.

a. Explain how you can work this out from the information given on the diagram.

_____

_____

100 J of energy transferred to the TV by electricity

? J transferred by light

5 J transferred by sound

85 J transferred by heating

b. How much of the energy transferred each second is useful?

_____

_____

Ways of storing energy	Ways of transferring energy
chemical elastic potential (strain) gravitational potential kinetic nuclear (atomic) thermal	forces heating light sound

The diagram shows different ways of making a house more energy efficient.

1. Which of these things describes a more energy-efficient house compared with a less energy-efficient one? Tick **two** boxes.

☐ Less energy is transferred through the walls by heating.

☐ The house is always warm inside.

☐ Fuel bills are lower.

☐ It has gas central heating.

☐ Less energy is needed to heat it if both houses are kept at the same temperature.

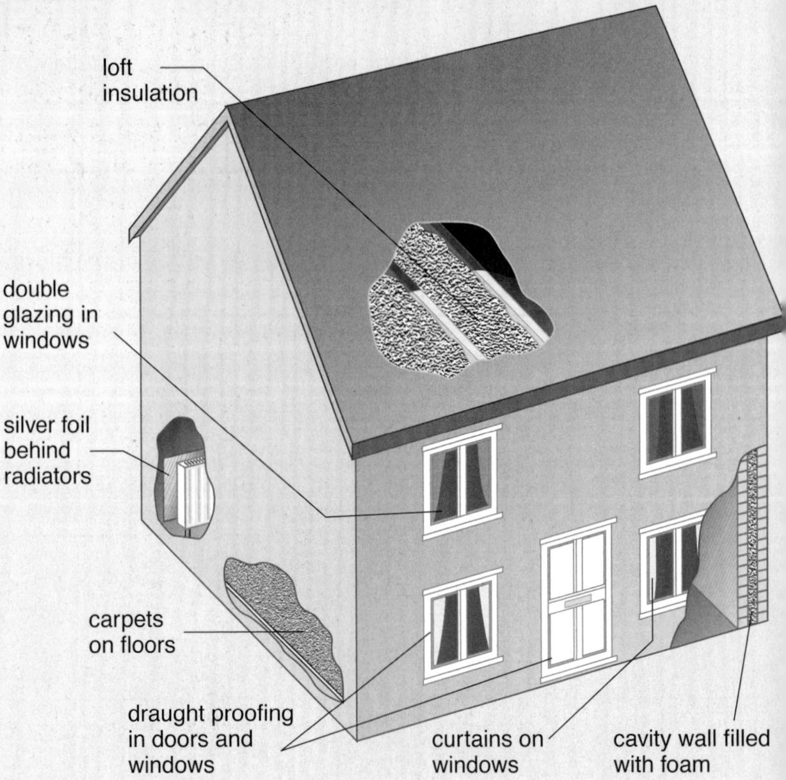

loft insulation

double glazing in windows

silver foil behind radiators

carpets on floors

draught proofing in doors and windows

curtains on windows

cavity wall filled with foam

2. Name one feature of the house that reduces the energy transferred by the following:

a. radiation _____

b. conduction _____

c. convection _____

3. Tick the boxes to show which statements are true and which are false.

	True	False
a. A material with a high **thermal conductivity** is a good insulator.	☐	☐
b. Energy can be transferred faster through thin walls than through thick walls.	☐	☐
c. Materials that contain trapped air are good **thermal conductors**.	☐	☐
d. **Insulation** can keep cold things cold.	☐	☐

4. Write corrected versions of the statements in question **3** that are false.

_____

_____

_____

5. Explain your answer to **3c**.

_____

_____

Pollution-free motoring!

The new *Zap!* car has batteries instead of a fuel tank. Just plug in for a couple of hours and you are set for miles of pollution-free motoring! No carbon-dioxide emissions!

Our electric car has an efficiency of 0.75 compared with only around 0.15 for a petrol-driven car.

---

1. Electric cars use energy stored in a battery. _____

a. Is electricity a fuel? Explain your answer. _____

_____

b. What fuel do most cars use? _____

c. Give one advantage of this fuel when used in cars. _____

d. Give one disadvantage of using this fuel. _____

2. Electricity is generated in power stations and can also be generated using **renewable** resources.

a. Name **two fossil fuels** that are used in fossil fuel power stations._____

b. Give another use for one of these fuels. _____

c. What gas do these fuels emit when they burn? _____

d. What problem is this gas partly responsible for? _____

e. Name a type of fuel used in power stations that does not emit this gas. _____

3. Is it true to say that the *Zap!* car does not cause any pollution when it is used? Explain your answer.

_____

_____

4. The efficiency of the *Zap!* car is given as 0.75. What does this mean? Tick one box.

☐ It wastes 75 J of energy for every 100 J stored in the battery.

☐ It transfers 75 J of useful energy for every 100 J stored in the battery.

☐ It transfers 75 J of energy altogether for every 100 J stored in the battery.

5. An electric car is charged using electricity from a fossil-fuelled power station with an efficiency of 0.5. Some energy is also transferred by heating in the wires that carry the electricity from the power station to the place where the car is charged.

a. Which do you think is the true efficiency of the electric car when you think about the energy stored in the fossil fuel:

☐ $0.5 \times 0.75 = 0.375$ ☐ $0.5 + 0.75 = 1.25$ ☐ less than 0.375?

b. Is the electric car really more efficient than a petrol-driven car? Explain your answer.

_____

_____

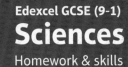

1. The diagrams show a Slinky spring being used to model different kinds of wave.

Label the diagrams using words from the box. You can use each word once, more than once, or not at all.

a. _____ wave

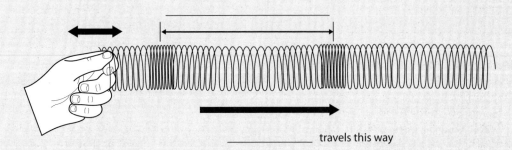

amplitude	energy	frequency	longitudinal
particles	period	transverse	wavelength

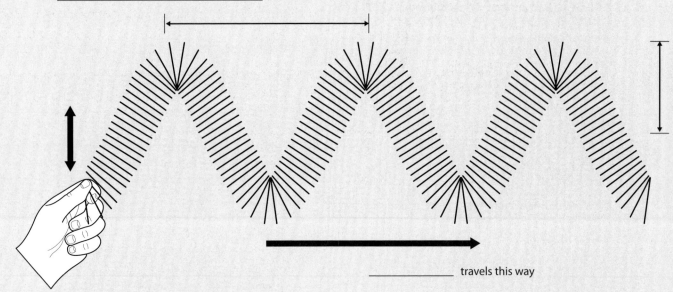

_____ travels this way

b. _____ wave

_____ travels this way

2. Give **two** examples of each type of wave.

a. longitudinal (i)_____ (ii) _____

b. transverse   (i)_____ (ii) _____

3. The sentences below all contain mistakes. Make changes to correct the mistakes. The first sentence has been corrected for you.

      longitudinal   *and forwards*

a. In a ~~transverse~~ wave, the particles move backwards ⋀ in the same direction as the wave is travelling.

b. Waves transfer energy and matter.

c. The amplitude of a transverse wave is the distance from the top to the bottom of the wave.

d. The frequency of a wave is the time it takes for one complete wave to go past.

e. The period of a wave is measured in hertz.

Sciences **CP4c** Refraction
Homework & skills

1. Draw lines to match up the sentence halves.

a. Refraction can happen when a wave…	…is similar to refraction when light goes from air into glass.
b. The normal is a line…	…it bends away from the normal.
c. When light travels from air into water…	…its direction does not change.
d. When light travels from water into air…	…crosses an interface between two different materials.
e. Refraction when light goes from air into water…	…drawn at right angles to an interface.
f. If a ray of light crosses an interface at right angles…	…it bends towards the normal.

2. The drawing shows light entering a block of glass.

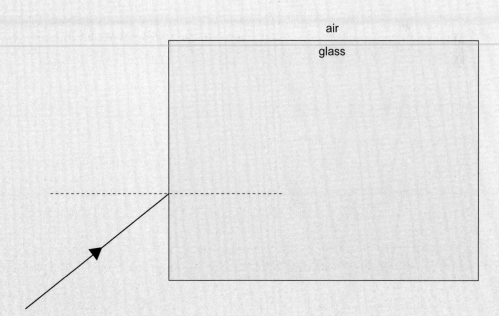

a. What does the dashed line represent?_____

b. Continue drawing the ray of light to show what happens when the light goes into the glass and comes out again on the other side.

This table of results is from an experiment like the one that William Herschel did in 1800. One thermometer was placed in different parts of a spectrum of light and left for 10 minutes. The temperature was recorded every two minutes. First, the thermometer bulb was placed in the blue light, then in the yellow light, and finally it was used to measure the temperature just beyond the red colour.

Colour	Temperature (°C)						
	at start	2 min	4 min	6 min	8 min	10 min	overall rise
blue	19	21	21	23	25	25	
yellow	19	20	18	25	28	28	
beyond red	19	25	27	30	30	30	

1. Calculate the overall temperature rise for each colour and write it in the table.

2. Plot a line graph of the results on the axes on the right. Draw a smooth curve through each set of points and label the lines on your graph.

3. Describe the results of the experiment.

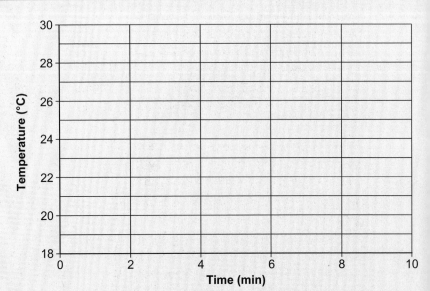

_____
_____
_____
_____
_____
_____

4. One of the results does not fit the pattern.

a. Draw a ring around this result. _____

b. Suggest how this may have happened. _____
_____

5. Identify a control variable in this experiment. _____

6. Suggest one way in which you could you change this experiment to improve the quality of your data.
_____
_____

7. Name the **electromagnetic waves** that are found just beyond:

a. red light _____

b. violet light. _____

1. Read the following story.

a. <u>Underline</u> all the places where radio waves are used.

b. Draw a box around the places where microwaves are used.

c. Draw a wiggly line under the places were infrared is used.

d. Shade the places where visible light is used.

Cyril's magazine had an interesting story about a radio telescope looking for possible signals from aliens. He put the magazine down to get his porridge out of the microwave. At the same time the toaster popped up. His toast was burnt again. He switched off the radio and took his breakfast into the living room to watch TV.

He pressed the remote to switch on. There was a news report from the USA, live by satellite. Cyril shivered with the cold and switched the electric fire on. He could feel the warmth as soon as he pressed the switch. He was soon bored with the news and changed channel to watch *Amazing Police Chases*. There was a view from a police helicopter at night. The suspects showed up as light-coloured blobs in the thermal image. When the suspects moved onto open ground the pilot switched on a searchlight so that the officers on the ground could see more easily. The chase was just getting really exciting when Cyril's phone vibrated; it was Anya saying Cyril had to leave now to meet her on the way to school.

2. All the long waves in the electromagnetic spectrum are used in communication. Which part (or parts) of the electromagnetic spectrum is used:

a. to transmit mobile phone signals _____

b. to transmit radio and TV broadcasts _____

c. to send information along optical fibres _____

d. by lighthouses to warn ships of danger _____

e. to send remote control signals to TVs? _____

3. How can we detect:

a. visible light _____

b. infrared radiation _____

c. microwaves and radio waves? _____

Shoe-fitting fluoroscopes were first used in shoe shops about 80 years ago. They consisted of a wooden box with a hole at the bottom where you put your feet. When you looked through a hole on the top, you could see an image of the bones of your feet and the outline of the shoes. This picture was made by an X-ray scanner.

The fluoroscope was an X-ray tube. X-rays have very high frequency, so are very high energy – and we now know they can cause cancer after long-term exposure. The only protection between your feet and the tube was a 1 mm thick sheet of aluminium.

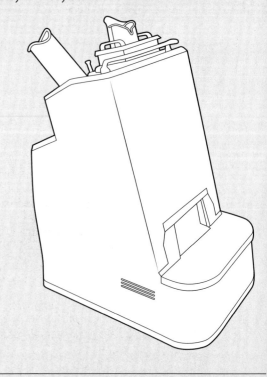

Despite high exposures, there were no reported health problems from shoe-shop customers. Unfortunately, many shoe salespeople put their hands into the X-ray beam to feel the shoe during the fitting. One salesperson, who had operated a fluoroscope 10 to 20 times each day over a 10-year period, developed a skin disorder. A shoe model received such a serious radiation burn that her leg had to be removed. These machines were used in Britain until around 1970.

1. Look through the text and underline any points that explain what the fluoroscope was used for.

2. Circle any points that suggest X-rays can be dangerous.

3. When were these machines in use in shoe shops? _____

4. Why did shoe shops stop using them? _____

_____

5. Why were salespeople more at risk than customers who used the shoe-fitting machines?

_____

_____

6. How can you tell from the text that X-rays can pass through a 1 mm thickness of aluminium?

_____

_____

7. a. Name one part of the electromagnetic spectrum with a higher frequency than X-rays. _____

b. Would these waves be more or less harmful than X-rays? Explain your answer. _____

_____

8. What harm can X-rays do to the body? _____

Sciences   CP6a Atomic models
Homework & skills

1. These names describe three models of the **atom**. Write a number next to each model to show the order in which they were suggested, with 1 showing the earliest.

☐ plum pudding model   ☐ Rutherford's model   ☐ atoms as spheres

2. Tick (✔) the correct columns to show which statements apply to each model.

	Plum pudding model	Rutherford's model	Atoms as spheres
a. An atom is a solid sphere.	☐	☐	☐
b. An atom consists of parts with negative and positive charges.	☐	☐	☐
c. Negative charges in the atom are called electrons.	☐	☐	☐
d. The atom is a mass of positively charged material with electrons scattered through it.	☐	☐	☐
e. Most of the atom is empty space.	☐	☐	☐
f. The mass of the atom is concentrated in a central nucleus.	☐	☐	☐
g. The positive charge in an atom is concentrated in the central nucleus.	☐	☐	☐

3. One of Rutherford's experiments fired **alpha particles** at gold foil. Which statement explains what Rutherford should have found if the plum pudding model were correct?

☐ Some particles could bounce back from the atomic nuclei.

☐ All the alpha particles would go through the foil, because there would not be enough mass concentrated in one place to deflect them.

4. Which **two** of the following statements describe what Rutherford did find in his experiment?

☐ Some alpha particles passed straight through the foil.

☐ All the alpha particles passed straight through the foil.

☐ All the alpha particles were scattered through large angles.

☐ Some alpha particles were scattered, some of them by large angles.

5. Explain Rutherford's results by drawing lines to match the sentence halves.

The particles that went straight through …   … passed close to the positively charged nucleus.

The particles that were deflected by small angles …   … passed through the empty space between the nucleus and the electrons in the atoms.

The particles that were deflected by large angles …   … hit the dense, positively charged nucleus.

1. The diagrams show how electrons can change position in atoms when they absorb or emit energy. The diagrams all represent atoms of the same element.

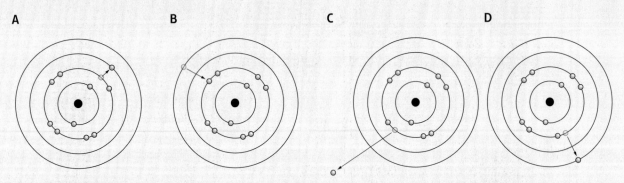

A   B   C   D

a. Which diagram (or diagrams) shows an electron moving to a higher **orbit**? _____

b. Which diagram (or diagrams) shows an electron moving to a lower orbit? _____

c. Which diagram (or diagrams) shows an atom emitting energy? _____

d. Which diagram (or diagrams) show an atom absorbing energy? _____

e. Which diagram (or diagrams) show an atom becoming an **ion**? _____

2. Look at diagram A.

a. How many electrons does this atom have? _____

b. What is the overall charge on an atom? _____

c. How many protons does this atom have in its nucleus? _____

d. Explain how you worked out your answer to part **c**. _____

_____

e. What charge will this atom have when it loses an electron? _____

f. Explain your answer to part **e**. _____

_____

_____

_____

3. The box on the right describes four different models of the atom.

a. Which one is the best description of the Rutherford model? _____

b. Which one is the best description of Bohr's model? _____

c. What evidence does Bohr's model explain that Rutherford's does not?

A. An atom consists of a nucleus containing protons and neutrons, with electrons in fixed orbits around the nucleus.

B. Atoms are a 'pudding' of positive charge with tiny negative charges embedded in it.

C. Atoms are solid spheres.

D. Atoms have most of their mass in a positively charged nucleus with electrons moving around it.

_____

_____

Sciences
CP6e Types of radiation
Homework & skills

The diagram shows an experiment in which three different materials were placed in front of three radioactive sources. Remember that **alpha particles** have a positive charge, **beta particles** have a negative charge and **gamma rays** have no charge.

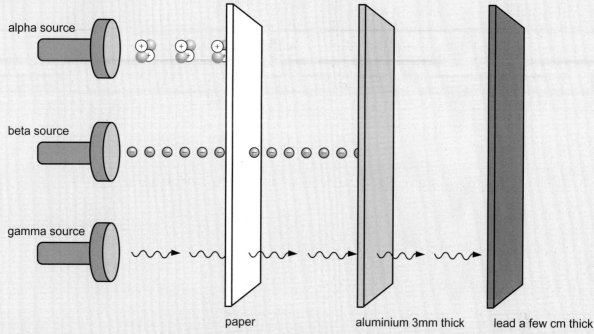

paper   aluminium 3mm thick   lead a few cm thick

1. Complete the table of how **penetrating** and ionising different radiations are, using the diagram above. For the last two columns, use the words 'highly', 'partly' or 'slightly'.

Radiation	Blocked by	Penetrating	Ionising
alpha			
beta			
gamma			

2. The boxes show different types of radiation that **unstable** nuclei can emit.

alpha particle	beta particle	**positron**	neutron	gamma ray

a. Write a "P" in the boxes of all the types of radiation that are particles.

b. Write a "+" for all the types of radiation that have a positive charge, and a "–" for the ones with a negative charge.

c. Write a "1" for the types of radiation that have a mass equal to or greater than 1.

3. Complete the following sentences using the words in the box.

decay   gains   ions   loses   **random**   unstable

Ionising radiation is emitted from _____ nuclei. The process is _____. This means you cannot predict

when the nucleus will _____ and emit radiation. This radiation can cause atoms to become _____.

Ionisation occurs when an atom _____ or _____ electrons.

4. Smoke detectors used in homes contain a source of alpha particles. Explain why the radiation from smoke detectors does not harm people living in the house.

_____

_____

The **half-life** is how long it takes for half of the undecayed nuclei in a sample of radioactive material to decay.

The graph on the right shows the **activity** of a radioactive source over time. Use it to answer questions **1** and **2**.

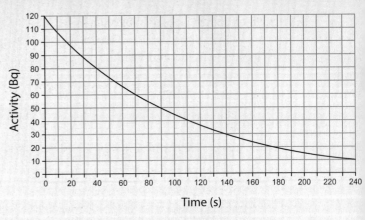

1. How long does it take for the radioactivity to drop:

a. from 120 to 60 counts per second

_____

b. from 80 to 40 counts per second

c. from 50 to 25 counts per second?

_____   _____

2. What do you notice about your values in question **1**? Explain your answer.

_____

_____

3. Work out the half-lives of the radioactive isotopes shown on each of these graphs. Show your working.

a.

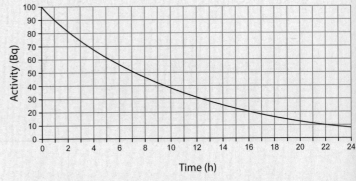

half-life: _____

b.

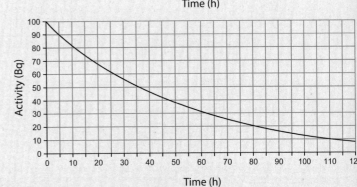

half-life: _____

The half-life of fermium-253 is 3 days.

4. A sample of fermium-253 contains 400 000 atoms. How many undecayed nuclei are left after:

a. 3 days _____

b. 6 days _____

c. 12 days? _____

5. A sample of fermium-253 has 100 000 atoms. How long will it take for the number of undecayed atoms to reduce to:

a. 50 000 _____

b. 25 000? _____

Sciences
Homework & skills

CP7a Work and power

1. a. What are the units for **work done**? _____

b. What is the unit for **power**? _____

c. How is the unit for power connected to the unit for **energy**? _____

_____

2. Name three ways in which energy can be transferred. One has been done for you.

by forces

_____   _____   _____

3. Sam and Jill climb 6 m up into a tree. Sam uses a rope to pull up his bag with their lunch in it.

a. Sam's weight is 550 N. How much work does he do when he climbs the tree?

_____

b. Sam's bag weighs 20 N. How much work does he do when he pulls the bag up?

_____

c. Sam and Jill are the same weight. Jill climbs the tree faster than Sam. Explain who has exerted the greater power.

_____

_____

d. It takes Sam five seconds to pull his bag up. How much power has he used?

_____

_____

4. Priya pushes a crate along the floor with a force of 50 N. She does work of 450 N.

a. How far did she push the crate?

_____

_____

b. Priya's power was 25 W. How long did it take her to push the crate?

_____

_____

- -

work done = force × distance moved in direction of force	power = $\dfrac{\text{work done}}{\text{time taken}}$
E = work done in J F = force in N d = distance in m	E = work done in N P = power in W t = time in s

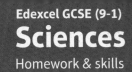

1. Forces can be **contact forces** or **non-contact forces**.

    a. Write the names of **two** non-contact forces. _____

    b. Write the names of **two** contact forces. _____

2. We can use an arrow to represent a force. Force is a **vector** quantity.

    What **two** pieces of information does an arrow show about a force?

    _____

    _____

3. Velocity is a vector quantity, and speed is a **scalar** quantity. The speed of a car is 20 m/s. What other information do you need in order to know the velocity of the car?

    _____

4. The diagram shows the Sun and the Earth.
    The Earth attracts the Sun, and the Sun attracts the Earth.

    a. What is the name of the force that causes this attraction?

    _____

    b. Draw **two** arrows on the diagram to show the forces between the Sun and the Earth. (*Hint:* remember that the length of the arrows represents the size of the force.)

5. The diagram shows two **magnets**. If two similar poles of a magnet are close to each other, they repel.

    Draw pairs of arrows on the diagrams to show the forces between the magnets.

    a

    b

6. What is the name for the space around a magnet where the magnet can affect other magnets or **magnetic materials**?

    _____

7. Which is the best description of where **gravitational fields** occur? Tick (✔) one.

    ☐ around planets and stars
    ☐ around the Earth and the Moon
    ☐ around objects that have mass
    ☐ around very heavy objects

1. Match diagrams **1–6** with circuits **a–f** below.

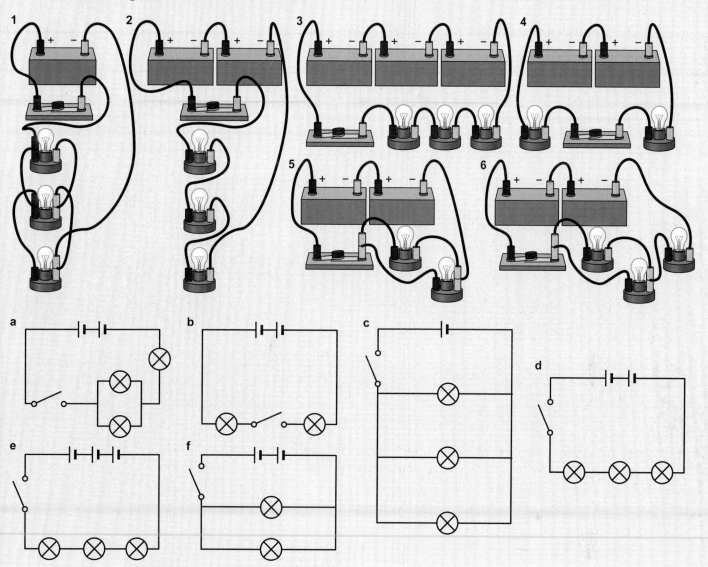

2. Draw a circuit diagram for the following circuit.

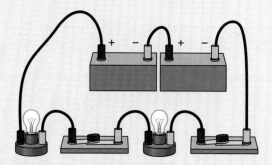

3. The diagram on the right shows a model of an **atom**.
Label the diagram with words from the box.

electron
negative charge
nucleus
neutron
positive charge
proton

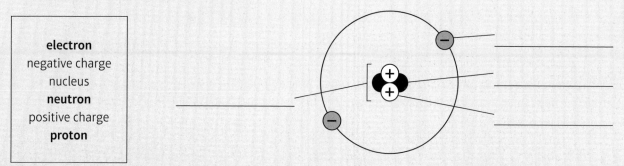

Sciences   **CP9b** Current and potential difference

Homework & skills

1. a. What does an **ammeter** measure? _____

b. What does a **voltmeter** measure? _____

c. Complete this circuit diagram to show how you would connect an ammeter to measure the current through the lamp and a voltmeter to measure the **potential difference** across the lamp.

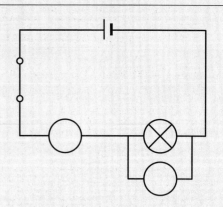

 2. In the following circuits, what are the missing current readings on the ammeters?

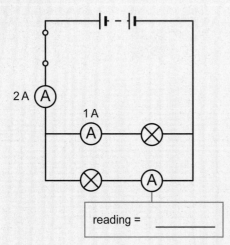

2 A

1 A

reading = _____

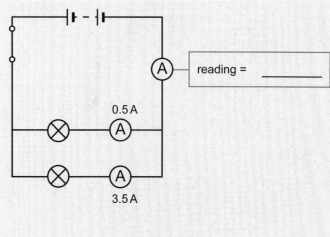

reading = _____

0.5 A

3.5 A

 3. In the following circuits, what are the missing potential differences on the voltmeters?

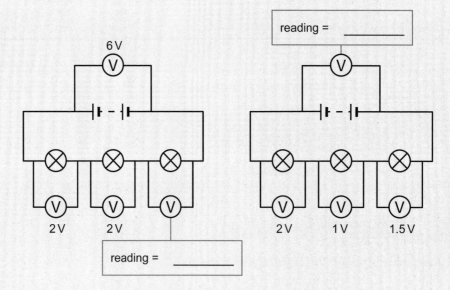

6 V

2 V   2 V

reading = _____

reading = _____

2 V   1 V   1.5 V

 4. Complete these sentences about identical lamps by choosing the correct words in italic.

When two lamps are connected in parallel, the potential difference across each lamp is *the same as / bigger than / smaller than* for one lamp on its own. The current through each lamp is the *same as / half / twice* the total current.

When two identical lamps are connected in series, the potential difference across each lamp is *the same as / half / twice* the total potential difference. The current through each lamp is *half / twice / the same as* the current for one lamp on its own.

1. Which component is each phrase below describing? Choose your answers from the box. You may use each component once, more than once or not at all.

| diode   filament lamp   light-dependent resistor   thermistor   light-emitting diode   variable resistor |

a. The resistance can be changed by moving a slider or a dial. _____

b. The resistance increases when there is a high potential difference and the component glows. _____

_____

c. The resistance gets less when it gets warmer. _____

d. It will only conduct electricity in one direction. _____ and _____

e. The resistance is highest in the dark. _____

f. This is the symbol for a _____

g. This is the symbol for a _____

h. This is the symbol for a _____

2. You have a circuit with a variable resistor in it. How will the current in the circuit change if you increase the resistance? _____

3. Cross out the incorrect answers in the following sentences.

a. The potential difference across a fixed resistor is 10 V. There is a 2 A current flowing through it. The resistance of the resistor is (0.5 Ω / 2 Ω / 5 Ω / 10 Ω / 50 Ω).

b. What will happen to the current if the potential difference doubles? (it doubles / it halves / it stays the same)

c. When the potential difference across a fixed resistor doubles, the current (doubles / halves / stays the same). This is because the resistance (doubles / halves / stays the same).

4. Choose words from the box to complete the sentences that explain how current and resistance change when potential difference is increased.

| decreases   increases   stays the same |

a. When the potential difference across a filament lamp is increased it glows more brightly. The resistance of the filament _____. This means that the current _____, but not by as much as it would in a fixed resistor.

b. If a **diode** is conducting and the potential difference is reversed the current _____ to zero.

c. When the diode is conducting, if the potential difference is increased the current _____ by a large amount.

5. Write down a use for:

a. a diode _____

b. a **light-dependent resistor** (LDR) _____

c. a **thermistor** _____

6. Complete these sentences.

a. When the light intensity on a light-dependent resistor (LDR) increases, its resistance _____.

b. When the temperature of a thermistor increases, its resistance _____.

1. Use words from the box to complete the sentences. Use each word once, more than once or not at all.

| amps | current | energy | joules | potential difference | second | time taken | volts | watts |

a. **Power** is the _____ transferred per _____.

b. Power is measured in _____.

c. Power = \dfrac{\text{_____ transfer}}{\text{_____}}

d. The power transfer in any circuit is equal to the _____ across it multiplied by the _____ through it.

2. Calculate:

a. the power of a blender that transfers 18 000 J in 60 s. Power = _____

b. the time that a 1000 W iron takes to transfer 300 000 J of energy. Give your answer in minutes.

_____

3. Write down the equation linking power with current and potential difference.

_____

4. Calculate:

a. the power transfer in a lamp that has a current of 2 A when the potential difference across it is 12 V.

_____

b. the current in a mains 2 kW fan heater (mains voltage = 230 V). _____

5. Write down the equation linking power, current and resistance.

_____

6. The power loss in a cable is the power transferred in heating the surroundings.

a. Calculate the power loss in a cable with a resistance of 100 W carrying a current of 5 A.

_____

b. Calculate the maximum resistance allowed for a cable carrying a current of 8 A if the power loss must not be more than 6400 W.

_____

7. A filament bulb has a **power rating** of 18 W and requires a potential difference of 9 V. Calculate:

a. the energy transferred when the lamp is on for 10 seconds _____

b. the current in the lamp _____

c. the resistance of the lamp. _____

1. This question is about a three-pin plug.

a. Label the part shown by the label line and explain what it is for.

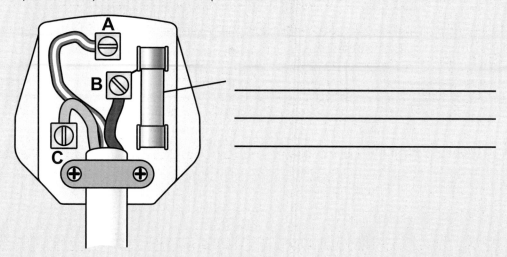

_____

_____

_____

b. Use the diagram to help you complete the table below.

Pin	Name of wire	Colour of wire	Voltage (V)
A			
B			
C		blue	

2. Complete these sentences. Some require single words, others require more writing.

a. A **fuse** _____ when the current gets too _____, and this _____ the circuit.

b. The metal case of an appliance is connected to the _____ wire. If the case becomes live, a

large _____ flows and melts the _____. This prevents a person from getting an

electric _____ from touching the _____.

c. A **circuit breaker** is an automatic _____ that switches _____ a circuit if there is

a fault such as too _____ a current.

d. A fuse that has a current rating that is too low will _____

_____

_____

e. A fuse that has a current rating that is too high will _____

_____

_____

1. Circle the materials in the box that are **magnetic materials**.

| aluminium | cobalt | copper | iron | nickel | steel |

2. The drawings show pairs of magnets. Write N and S on the unlabelled magnets to show how the magnets must be arranged to attract or repel each other.

a.

| S | N | | | |

attract

b.

| S | N | | | |

repel

3. The diagram shows **plotting compasses** being used to show the shape of a **magnetic field**.

a. Draw arrows in the compasses to show which way they would point. Two have been done for you. You can draw field lines on the diagram to help you, if you wish.

b. Draw an X on the diagram at one of the places where the field is strongest.

c. Explain how the diagram shows where the field is strongest.

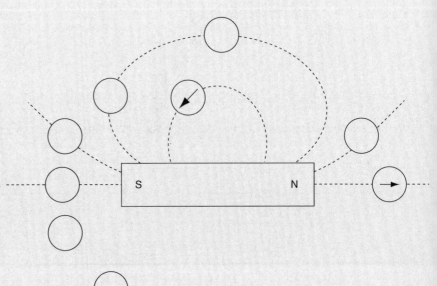

_____

_____

_____

4. Draw lines between the two magnets below to show a uniform magnetic field.

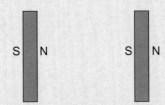

5. Tick the boxes to show which of these things are **permanent magnets** and which are **induced magnets**.

	Permanent magnet	Induced magnet
a. a compass needle		
b. paperclips picked up by a magnet		
c. bar magnet		

The diagram on the right shows a wire with current coming out of the page towards you. The grey line shows part of the magnetic field around the wire.

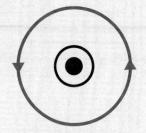

1. Where is the magnetic field around the wire strongest?

_____

2. Add **two** more lines to complete the shape of the magnetic field. Remember that your drawing should show where the field is strongest.

3. Explain how you could find out which way to draw the arrows on the lines to show the magnetic field.

_____

_____

_____

4. How would the magnetic field you have drawn be different if:

a. the current was flowing in the opposite direction _____

_____

b. the current was smaller? _____

_____

5. The diagram on the right shows a **solenoid** and its magnetic field.

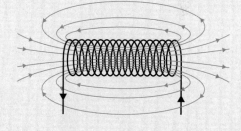

a. What type of permanent magnet has a similar field shape?

_____

b. Describe one way of making the field stronger.

_____

c. Which part of the magnetic field is a uniform field?

_____

d. Draw an N at one end of the solenoid to show which end acts as a north pole. Explain how you worked out your answer.

_____

6. You can put an iron core inside a solenoid. Explain why this iron core is referred to as a **temporary magnet**.

_____

_____

1. Electricity from power stations is transmitted around the country at a very high voltage. Why is this done? Tick **one** box.

☐ It is safer.　　　　　　　　　　☐ It is more dangerous.
☐ It wastes less energy.　　　　　☐ It wastes more energy.

2. Wasted energy is transferred from electricity lines by which of the following? Tick **one** box.

☐ light　　　　　　　　　　　　　☐ heating
☐ sound　　　　　　　　　　　　　☐ forces

3. Tick the correct boxes to show which kind of transformer is needed for each of these situations.

Starting voltage	Final voltage	Step-up transformer	Step-down transformer
25 kV	400 kV		
400 kV	33 kV		
33 kV	230 V		

4. Draw lines to match up the voltages with the descriptions.

230 V	voltage generated in power stations
11 kV	voltage in **transmission lines**
25 kV	voltage used by small factories
33 kV	voltage used by large factories
400 kV	voltage used in homes, shops and schools

5. This diagram represents the **national grid**.

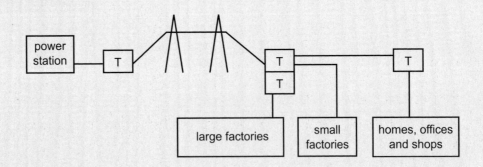

a. Each box labelled T represents a transformer. Next to each box, write SU or SD to show whether it is a **step-up transformer** (SU) or a **step-down transformer** (SD).

b. The voltages in the boxes in question **4** are the voltages in different parts of the national grid. Write the voltages in the correct places on the diagram above.

CP12a Particles and density

1. Diagrams A–E show a substance in different states.

Write the letters of the diagrams in order to show what happens when a gas is cooled to a liquid and then a solid.

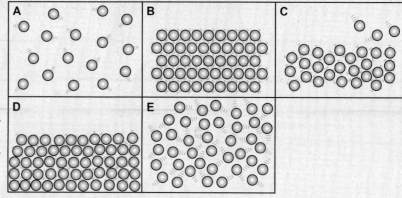

_____

_____

2. a. How do diagrams B and D show that solids and liquids cannot be **compressed**?

_____

b. What property (or properties) do liquids and gases have in common?

_____

3. Cross out the words that are wrong in these sentences.

A substance is usually (less/more) dense when it is a solid than when it is a liquid. This is because the particles are a little (closer together/further apart) in a liquid than a solid. The volume of the substance (increases/decreases) when it melts, and so the **density** (increases/decreases).

4. The triangle on the right can help you rearrange the equation used to calculate the density of a substance.

What do the letters represent? For each letter identify the correct unit.

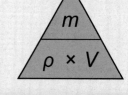

ρ represents _____ units _____

V represents _____ units _____

m represents _____ units _____

5. A block of concrete has a mass of 800 kg. Its volume is 0.6 m³. Calculate the density of the concrete.

$$\text{density} = \frac{\text{mass}}{\text{volume}}$$

=

density = _____ kg/m³

6. The density of sandstone is 2200 kg/m³. A statue made out of sandstone has a volume of 2 m³. Calculate the mass of the statue.

mass = _____ kg

Use these equations to help you answer the questions.

change in thermal energy (J) = mass (kg) × specific heat capacity (J/kg °C) × change in temperature (°C)

thermal energy needed for a change of state (J) = mass (kg) × specific latent heat (J/kg)

1. Some students have 100 g of ice. The temperature of the ice is –4 °C. They need to calculate how much energy they will need to heat the ice until it is all melted.

a. First, they calculate how much energy is needed to heat the ice to its melting point. Write down the equation they use to do this.

b. Next, they calculate how much energy is needed to melt the ice. Write down the equation they use to do this.

2. A saucepan contains 1.5 litres of water (mass = 1.5 kg). The temperature of the water is 10 °C.

| specific heat capacity of water = 4182 J/kg °C |
| specific latent heat of evaporation for water = 2 257 000 J/kg |

a. What is the temperature change if the water is heated to boiling point?

b. Calculate the energy required to heat the water to boiling point.

energy = _____ J

c. 50 000 J of energy is transferred to the water when it is at boiling point. Calculate the mass of water that evaporates.

mass = _____ kg

3. An ice cube has a temperature of 0 °C. Its mass is 0.01 kg. It takes 3340 J of energy to melt the ice. Calculate the specific latent heat of melting for ice.

specific latent heat = _____ J/kg

- -

| Q = thermal energy needed for a change of state (J)

m = mass (kg)

L = specific latent heat (J/kg) | 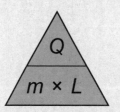 | ΔQ = change in thermal energy (J)

m = mass (kg)

c = specific heat capacity (J/kg °C)

$\Delta \theta$ = change in temperature | 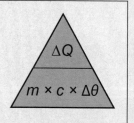 |

1. The table on the right shows the results of a stretching experiment.

a. Calculate the **extension** of the object for each force. Two have been done for you.

b. Plot the points on the graph grid below. Two have been done for you.

c. Join the points with a smooth curve.

Force (N)	Length (cm)	Extension (cm)
0	5.0	0.0
5	5.5	0.5
10	7.0	
15	9.0	
20	11.0	
25	12.0	
30	12.5	

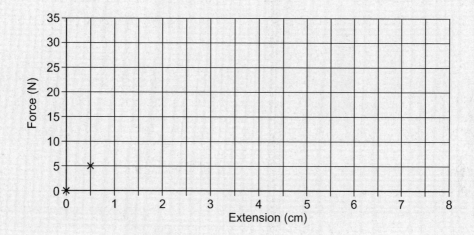

2. Is the object being tested a spring or a rubber band? _____

Explain your answer. _____

_____

3. **a.** Is the line on your graph showing a **linear** or a **non-linear relationship**? _____

b. Draw a line on your graph that shows a **directly proportional** relationship between force and extension.

4. A student rests a plastic ruler over the edge of a bench and flicks it to vibrate and make a sound.

a. Explain whether the ruler is behaving **elastically** or **inelastically** when the student bends it like this.

_____

_____

b. Give a different example of an object behaving:

   i   elastically _____

   ii inelastically._____

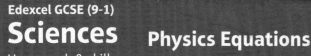
Recall and apply:

distance travelled = average speed × time

acceleration = $\dfrac{\text{change in velocity}}{\text{time taken}}$ $a = \dfrac{(v - u)}{t}$

force = mass × acceleration $F = m \times a$

weight = mass × gravitational field strength $W = m \times g$

efficiency = $\dfrac{\text{(useful energy transferred by the device)}}{\text{(total energy supplied to the device)}}$

wave speed = frequency × wavelength $v = f \times \lambda$

wave speed = distance ÷ time $v = \dfrac{x}{t}$

density = mass ÷ volume $\rho = \dfrac{m}{V}$

work done = force × distance moved in direction of force $E = F \times d$

change in gravitational potential energy
= mass × gravitational field strength × change in vertical height $\Delta GPE = m \times g \times \Delta h$

kinetic energy = ½ × mass × (speed)^2 $KE = \tfrac{1}{2} \times m \times v^2$

power = work done ÷ time taken $P = \dfrac{E}{t}$

energy transferred = charge moved × potential difference $E = Q \times V$

charge = current × time $Q = I \times t$

potential difference = current × resistance $V = I \times R$

| power = energy transferred ÷ time taken | $P = \dfrac{E}{t}$ |

| electrical power = current × potential difference | $P = I \times V$ |

| electrical power = (current)^2 × resistance | $P = I^2 \times R$ |

| force exerted on a spring = spring constant × extension | $F = k \times x$ |

Select and apply:

| (final velocity)^2 − (initial velocity)^2 = 2 × acceleration × distance | $v^2 - u^2 = 2 \times a \times x$ |

| energy transferred = current × potential difference × time | $E = I \times V \times t$ |

| For transformers with 100% efficiency, potential difference across primary coil × current in primary coil = potential difference across secondary coil × current in secondary coil | $V_p \times I_p = V_s \times I_s$ |

| change in thermal energy = mass × specific heat capacity × change in temperature | $\Delta Q = m \times c \times \Delta\theta$ |

| thermal energy for a change of state = mass × specific latent heat | $Q = m \times L$ |

| energy transferred in stretching = 0.5 × spring constant × (extension)^2 | $E = \frac{1}{2} \times k \times x^2$ |

The Periodic Table of the Elements

Key

| relative atomic mass |
| **atomic symbol** |
| name |
| atomic (proton) number |

Example:
| 1 |
| **H** |
| hydrogen |
| 1 |

1	2		3	4	5	6	7	0
								4 **He** helium 2
7 **Li** lithium 3	9 **Be** beryllium 4		11 **B** boron 5	12 **C** carbon 6	14 **N** nitrogen 7	16 **O** oxygen 8	19 **F** fluorine 9	20 **Ne** neon 10
23 **Na** sodium 11	24 **Mg** magnesium 12		27 **Al** aluminium 13	28 **Si** silicon 14	31 **P** phosphorus 15	32 **S** sulfur 16	35.5 **Cl** chlorine 17	40 **Ar** argon 18
39 **K** potassium 19	40 **Ca** calcium 20	45 **Sc** scandium 21 / 48 **Ti** titanium 22 / 51 **V** vanadium 23 / 52 **Cr** chromium 24 / 55 **Mn** manganese 25 / 56 **Fe** iron 26 / 59 **Co** cobalt 27 / 59 **Ni** nickel 28 / 63.5 **Cu** copper 29 / 65 **Zn** zinc 30	70 **Ga** gallium 31	73 **Ge** germanium 32	75 **As** arsenic 33	79 **Se** selenium 34	80 **Br** bromine 35	84 **Kr** krypton 36
85 **Rb** rubidium 37	88 **Sr** strontium 38	89 **Y** yttrium 39 / 91 **Zr** zirconium 40 / 93 **Nb** niobium 41 / 96 **Mo** molybdenum 42 / [98] **Tc** technetium 43 / 101 **Ru** ruthenium 44 / 103 **Rh** rhodium 45 / 106 **Pd** palladium 46 / 108 **Ag** silver 47 / 112 **Cd** cadmium 48	115 **In** indium 49	119 **Sn** tin 50	122 **Sb** antimony 51	128 **Te** tellurium 52	127 **I** iodine 53	131 **Xe** xenon 54
133 **Cs** caesium 55	137 **Ba** barium 56	139 **La*** lanthanum 57 / 178 **Hf** hafnium 72 / 181 **Ta** tantalum 73 / 184 **W** tungsten 74 / 186 **Re** rhenium 75 / 190 **Os** osmium 76 / 192 **Ir** iridium 77 / 195 **Pt** platinum 78 / 197 **Au** gold 79 / 201 **Hg** mercury 80	204 **Tl** thallium 81	207 **Pb** lead 82	209 **Bi** bismuth 83	[209] **Po** polonium 84	[210] **At** astatine 85	[222] **Rn** radon 86
[223] **Fr** francium 87	[226] **Ra** radium 88	[227] **Ac*** actinium 89 / [261] **Rf** rutherfordium 104 / [262] **Db** dubnium 105 / [266] **Sg** seaborgium 106 / [264] **Bh** bohrium 107 / [277] **Hs** hassium 108 / [268] **Mt** meitnerium 109 / [271] **Ds** darmstadtium 110 / [272] **Rg** roentgenium 111						

Elements with atomic numbers 112-116 have been reported but not fully authenticated.

*The lanthanoids (atomic numbers 58-71) and the actinoids (atomic numbers 90-103) have been omitted.

The relative atomic masses of copper and chlorine have not been rounded to the nearest whole number.